D0289525

# What others are saying about Jim Rohn...

*"I truly believe Jim Rohn is an extraordinary human being whose philosophy can enhance the quality of life for anyone who exposes themselves to it. He certainly had a positive impact on me at a time in my life when I was first forming the philosophies that guide me today."*
—Anthony Robbins, author of *Awaken the Giant Within*

*"Jim Rohn is the master motivator—he has style, substance, charisma, relevance, charm, and what he says makes a difference and it sticks. I consider Jim the 'Chairman of Speakers.' The world would be a better place if everyone heard my friend, Jim Rohn."*
—Mark Victor Hansen, co-author of *Chicken Soup for the Soul*

*"Jim Rohn is a national treasure and one of the most sought-after success experts ever. Why? Because his ideas work. They have worked so well that nearly an entire generation of personal-development trainers claim Jim as a mentor or a key influence."*
—Vic Conant, President of Nightingale-Conant

*"I've been a student of Jim Rohn since 1972. He was then—and still is—one of the most profound thinkers and mind-expanding individuals I've ever had a chance to listen to."*
—Les Brown, author of *Choosing Your Future*

*"Jim Rohn is one of the most articulate, powerful, thought-provoking speakers I've seen. His unique delivery and style puts him head and shoulders above the rest."*
—Harvey Mackay, author of *Swim with the Sharks Without Being Eaten Alive*

*"Jim is a modern-day Will Rogers. His perceptions of achievement and success have launched thousands of people on a wonderful, life-changing voyage into success and happiness. I can't recommend too strongly that you experience Jim Rohn personally."*
—Tom Hopkins, author of *How to Master the Art of Selling*

# What others are saying about Chris Widener...

*"Chris was very challenging and enriching. The leadership principles that he spoke on were at the very core of what we are trying to accomplish here on the HBS campus. Chris taught us the tenets of true leadership and how to immediately apply those truths in our own leadership situation. I would encourage everyone to learn from Chris Widener's Extraordinary Leaders seminar!"*
—John Lunde, Harvard Business School, Student Leader, MBA

*"I have spoken to more than 3,000 audiences, and I can tell you that Chris Widener is one of the best speakers in America today. He has wonderful content—extremely motivational, he is funny, he is sharp, he is quick and to the point. You'll love him, too."*
—Brian Tracy, author of *Eat That Frog*

*"Our people loved Chris and loved his material. He was extremely helpful and challenging. My sales team and I highly recommend him!"*
—Phil Castillo, Director, Northern Channels, Cisco Systems

*"Chris Widener has the talent, the articulation, the message, the presence, the ability! Chris Widener is one of the brand-new top stars on the international platform speaking circuit today."*
—Denis Waitley, author of *Seeds of Greatness*

*"Chris Widener is a powerful presenter, a quick wit, and a home run every time. He definitely challenges you to the next level in life and work."*
—Kevin Mather, CFO, MLB's Seattle Mariners

*"Chris Widener is nothing short of phenomenal—his patience, his knowledge, his ability to engage with an audience. Chris, you do an amazing job."*
—Jim Rohn, author of *The Five Major Pieces to the Life Puzzle*

# TWELVE
# PILLARS

A Novel by
## Jim Rohn and Chris Widener

# TWELVE **PILLARS**

Published by
Jim Rohn International and Chris Widener International
www.JimRohn.com
www.ChrisWidener.com

Distributed by
www.YourSuccessStore.com
200 Swisher Road
Lake Dallas, Texas 75065
877-929-0439

© Copyright by Jim Rohn International 2005, 2010

All rights reserved worldwide. No part of this book may be reproduced
or transmitted in any form or by any means, electronic or mechanical,
including photocopying, recording, or by any information storage
and retrieval system, without the written permission of the publisher,
except where permitted by law.

ISBN: 978-0-9726266-3-7  (Paperback)

Printed in the United States of America.

# TWELVE **PILLARS**

## Contents

# Dedication

*To Jim Rohn for giving of himself for so many years to so many people as he has traveled the world and developed the ideas that are shared within.*

*To Kyle Wilson and the extremely talented and dedicated staff at Jim Rohn International, for being the backbone of this project that made it possible. Hilary and Yveatte, your help on this book was invaluable!*

*To my wife, Lisa, and our four children for being such a fantastic family and the joy of my life!*

— **Chris Widener**

*To Chris Widener for his collaboration in taking this story of* Twelve Pillars *from concept to print, and all that goes in between. Chris, you are the next generation. Keep sharing your story, living, and teaching the principles of success and impacting lives.*

*To Kyle Wilson and the staff at JRI, including Hilary Overpeck, Charles Moore, Crystal Prince, Yveatte Moore, Mary Haviland, Greg Anderson, and the entire gang, for all you've done over the years and continue to do in spreading my message across the globe each day.*

*To the readers of my weekly e-zine, those who have purchased my books and audios and attended my seminars, you are my "why"... why I keep traveling and sharing the philosophies of success—to hear your stories, triumphs, and successes.*

*And to my family, thank you for graciously allowing me the time I spend away from you to travel the globe and share the philosophies and principles that impacted my life so many years ago. You inspire me!*

— **Jim Rohn**

# Preface

One of the greatest compliments ever paid to me was from a friend who said that the lessons on life and leadership that I teach are "timeless truths rather than vogue content." I believe that there are core principles of success, universal and timeless truths that men and women of every generation can apply to their lives that will help them succeed in every area of their lives.

This is why I am such a great admirer of Jim Rohn and so highly privileged to be able to co-author *Twelve Pillars* with him—it teaches the timeless truths of one of our generation's master motivators. Jim has traveled the world for over forty years teaching the principles and philosophies associated with the Twelve Pillars of Success. It is my honor to join him in putting those lessons into a fictional account so that future generations can glean the wisdom Jim has shared with people all over the globe.

Recognized in the 1980's and 1990's as America's foremost business philosopher, Jim Rohn's message has continued into the twenty-first century impacting millions of lives throughout the world, including many of the most respected business people, speakers, and writers. When he received the National Speakers Association's Master of Influence Award—the speaking profession's highest honor—in the summer of 2004, I realized just how influential Jim's words have been in shaping the thoughts and ideas of those who, in turn, shape the thoughts and ideas of millions of people everywhere.

So, whether this is your first introduction to Jim Rohn or if you have heard or read his works before, I invite you to sit down and enjoy his lessons in the form of the Twelve Pillars of Success. They are indeed timeless truths that, if you follow them, will surely lead you to a better life. As you reflect on each lesson, ask yourself how you may apply these truths in your own life. Turn these ideas into action, and they will change your life and career in ways you could never imagine.

Enjoy!

Chris Widener

I am often asked by those who attend my seminars, why, at my age, I keep traveling the globe, speaking and teaching. My answer is simply this: to leave a legacy.

Imagine with me, for a moment, if you will, long after I am gone, someone up in an attic somewhere going through a box of dusty, old books. They find one of mine, and something about the cover compels them to open it. Blowing off the dust, they idly thumb through the pages, until a sentence catches their eye and they begin to read. And as they read, the words leap off the page at them with life-changing principles, simple yet compelling, giving them the vision of who they can be, what they can become, a life they can design and dreams they can accomplish. In that moment, when a light dawns, miracles happen! That is my "why."

With this in mind, Chris Widener and I present to you, *Twelve Pillars*. We've attempted to blend together the fundamental principles and teachings I've been sharing for over 40 years, and weave them into a unique tapestry of a fictional account of three characters: Michael, Charlie, and Mr. Davis.

My hope (and Chris's) is that as you read this book, these Pillars will become the foundation upon which you build your current and future success and achievement. But then I ask you to take it one step further. As you master these Pillars of Success, take them and create your own legacy as you then in turn teach and train others in the same way, so that you, too, may have the exploding satisfaction that you've used your gifts wisely, that you've blessed yourself, your family, community, and your business along this journey that life sets before us all.

To your success!

Jim Rohn

# 1
# A Chance Encounter

*"The only way things are going to change for you is when you change."*

"Crud!"

His hand hit the dashboard as he said it. "I can't stand this car!"

That about sums up Michael Jones's life—crud. And... he can't stand it.

Forty years old, a wife of fifteen years he doesn't know how to connect with, and two kids he barely knows. Add to that a boring job that doesn't challenge him and hardly pays the bills. In a word: crud.

Where had his life gone? Out of college, he and his wife, Amy, had been so filled with dreams. Their lives were ahead of them and nothing seemed impossible. They were full of potential and wanted to do so much. But now they were nowhere near where they had hoped to be.

Michael loved Amy, but it just wasn't what it could be. They had grown apart through the years, and he had no idea how to fix it. The kids are great but, again, there was just no connection with them like he thought "normal" families should have.

And his job... definitely not what he wanted. A man his age making $40,000 a year with no upside? This was hardly what he had imagined for his life. It was what it was, and it seemed like he was stuck—stuck with a dead-end job and poor relationships. This wasn't the success and happiness he and Amy had planned for.

But his life was about to change...

*This car is the worst,* he thought as it convulsed and finally died. Going about 30 miles an hour when it stopped running, he guided it as it coasted to a stop along the road.

He was on his way to a sales call and he had never taken this road before. It was a long, winding road that acted as a shortcut between two major roads. Not many houses on *this* road, he observed.

After the car rolled to a stop, Michael got out and walked around the car. It wasn't as though he would be able to tell what was wrong from walking around, he knew zero about cars. He knew how to put gas in it, turn the key over and that was about it. *No smoke*, he thought, *and that had to be good.*

He popped the hood and looked at the engine. All the wires seemed connected. All the caps were on. He didn't have any idea what to do.

*I should have taken shop class in high school*, he thought.

Michael reached inside his jacket for his cell phone. He figured he would call a mechanic friend he knew and see if he could get some help. He flipped the phone open and saw the worst—no cell coverage there!

"Just my luck," he said out loud. "They can put a man on the moon and clone a sheep, but they can't put a cell site up where I need it."

He looked around trying to decide which way to start walking. Up ahead about 200 feet was a bend in the road and he couldn't see what was farther on so he decided to go that way, just hoping there might be a house beyond the bend.

As he walked, he kicked the gravel along the road.

Frustrated, alone, and stuck. That's how he felt right now. About this situation and life in general.

As he turned the corner, Michael came across something he had never seen in real life before. Sure, he had seen many in magazines and on TV, but never something like this with his own eyes.

*Nice pad.* Michael found himself standing in front of the most beautiful home he had ever seen. "Home" may not even be the right word for it. Right at the roadside was a huge gated entrance.

The large brick and wrought-iron fence stretched at least 500 feet along the roadside. And the gate was at least 10 feet high. Behind the gate was a house that had to be over 10,000 square feet. It was a white plantation-style that had twelve two-story pillars across the front—which made sense since the sign at the side of the gate said, "Twelve Pillars." It was magnificent. Michael stood in front of the gate for a few minutes, just looking in awe at the structure.

Finally he snapped back to reality and realized that he had to get his car fixed. He didn't see any other houses nearby, but he didn't know how to get to the house in front of him either.

Just then he saw an old man in white overalls emerge from what looked like a workshop just to the right of the driveway. The old man walked toward the gate.

When he got about 25 feet from the gate, the old man spoke, "Can I help you, young man?"

"Uh, yeah. I mean, I hope so. My car broke down, and I can't call anyone because my cell phone doesn't work out here. Can I borrow a phone?"

"Well, why don't you let me take a look at the car first? Maybe I can fix it."

The old man was about seventy, Michael figured. About 5 feet 11 inches. Medium build. Pretty good shape, it looked like. He was obviously the caretaker for the mansion.

The old man opened the gate with a push of a button on a remote he pulled from his overalls. When he walked through, he asked Michael where the car was.

"Just back around the bend," he said, pointing back down the road.

The old man stuck his hand out and introduced himself. "Charlie's my name. What's yours?"

"Michael. Nice to meet you."

As they walked, Charlie prodded for more information. "What kind of business are you in?"

"Sales."

"You make a good living at that?"

"No, not really."

The old man was silent for a moment and then asked, "Do you have a wife and kids?"

"Yes, a wife and two kids."

"Well, that's good."

When they reached the car, Charlie popped the hood and looked around, fiddling with wires.

"Let me try to start her," Charlie said.

Michael gave Charlie the keys, and he turned it over a few times, but it wouldn't start. The gas gauge read ½, but Charlie suspected that it was broken and the problem was that Michael was out of gas.

"Well, everything seems to be in order, so I am betting that you are out of gas and your gas gauge is just broken. Let's go get some gas from the workshop."

Michael didn't think that could possibly be the problem, but he had no other options at this point, so he said, "Okay, let's do it."

They began to walk back to the workshop together. As they passed through the gates, Michael asked about the house and owner. "So, who owns the house?"

"One Mr. Davis owns that house. Built it twenty years ago with his wife. Very successful businessman. Owns a bunch of different businesses—he has his hands in a lot of different things."

"Must be quite successful. How big is the house?"

"Fourteen thousand square feet in the main house. You can't see it, but there is a pool and pool house that is about 4,000 square feet and a 1,500-square-foot guest cottage in back."

"Wow," Michael replied. "He must have a lot of money."

"Yep, it's something alright. But Mr. Davis isn't just about money. He prides himself on being successful in everything in life. Life is more than just money."

"That's easy to say if you have some," Michael said.

"I can see that, but Mr. Davis was successful before he got his money. In fact, do you see those pillars along the front of the house? Each one represents a different area of success that Mr. Davis says is important for life. He built the house that way to represent his philosophy on life."

"Oh yeah? That's pretty cool, I guess."

Just then, they arrived at the workshop.

"Would you like a cup of coffee?" Charlie asked. "I just brewed a pot before I saw you standing at the gate."

"Sure, I'll take a cup."

Michael looked around. The workshop was almost as big as his house. It had every tool you could possibly imagine.

"How do you like it?"

"Oh, black, thanks," Michael replied.

Charlie poured the cup and then brought it to him. "There you go."

"Thanks." Michael took a sip and looked out the window at the main house. "I sure would love to be that successful."

"I am sure you could be if you wanted to," Charlie said.

"Well, I have given it my best shot the last 18 years, and it doesn't seem to have done much."

"You've worked hard, have you?" Charlie asked.

"I have worked very hard—harder than most. I work long hours, work overtime, everything."

"That may be your problem," Charlie suggested.

"Working hard is a problem?" Michael asked, looking confused.

"No, working hard isn't a problem in and of itself, but Mr. Davis always says that the first Pillar of Success is to work harder on yourself than you do on your job."

"I don't get it," Michael said.

"Mr. Davis has those twelve Pillars of Success I was telling you about. The first one he talks about is Personal Development. Success comes when you develop yourself beyond where you currently are. So you have to work harder on yourself—improving yourself—than you do on your job."

"But I was always told that if you work hard, keep your nose to the grindstone, and eventually you will get ahead. That isn't true?"

"Not exactly. You see, you will get the job in a company—and the salary that goes with it—that you deserve because of the level of skill you have. So you can work as hard as you want, long hours and everything, but as long as you stay at the same skill level, you will never go beyond that level of pay and promotion."

"So how do I get ahead?"

"You start working on yourself."

"Maybe I don't get it yet," Michael said, taking another sip of coffee.

"Okay, let me explain," Charlie offered. "You say you're in sales, right?"

"Yep."

"Okay, you make a certain amount of money based on how good a salesman you are. You can work harder and harder, but you will only make so much because you are only so good. The key is to become a *better salesman*. The way to do that is not to put in five more hours of work on your job. It is to start putting more work into yourself, Michael. Work harder on yourself than you do on your job."

"So how do I do that?"

"Read books, attend seminars, study the best salespeople. And then apply the information. Implement what you learn. Work on integrating the ideas into your everyday work. That way, when you make the same ten sales calls each day, you get more sales because you are a better salesman."

"Hmmm." Michael stared out the window at the mansion in the distance. Then he turned to Charlie. "How did you get so smart?" he said with a smile.

"I'm just telling you what Mr. Davis says. Work harder on yourself than you do on your job. Develop yourself." After he finished,

Charlie began to cough. At first, Michael thought he got something caught in this throat, but it was more than that.

"Are you okay?" Michael asked.

He waited at least a minute as Charlie finished coughing. "I'm okay. Sometimes I just get a coughing fit. That's all."

"Good. You had me worried there for a moment." Michael paused before getting back to his train of thought. "Okay, so, what else does Mr. Davis say about personal development?"

Charlie chuckled. "Well, he says a lot of things, Michael."

"So give me some. I need all the help I can get."

"Why do you think you need so much help?"

"I'm stuck. I loathe my job. I feel like I have no upside. I don't feel like I provide very well for my family. My car breaks down on the side of the road. You name it. I need help making my life better. I have worked so hard, and I still just seem to be spinning my wheels." The words spilled out so fast it surprised even Michael.

"Since you put it that way, let me think." Charlie paused and looked up at the ceiling. After a few moments, he raised his right index finger. "Here's one for you," he said. "Let me make sure I get it right now. Mr. Davis says, 'Every life form seems to strive to its maximum except human beings. How tall will a tree grow? As tall as it possibly can. Human beings, on the other hand, have been given the dignity of choice. They can choose to be all, or they can choose to be less. Why not stretch up to the full measure of the challenge and see all you can do?' " Charlie smiled, proud that he got it just right.

"But I have tried," Michael protested.

"I am not suggesting that you haven't. Maybe you have. The idea is that most people quit. Maybe you have given up, Michael. That is my impression anyway. With all due respect, it sounds as though you have worked hard, found that you are stuck, and perhaps have given up. Maybe it is time to stretch and to grow again."

Michael tilted his head back and finished the last bit of his coffee and then set the cup down on the table. "Yeah, maybe so. Maybe so. I just want things to change for me and my family."

Charlie stood up and began to walk to the back door. "Come with me. We'll get you some gas, and on the way back to the car, I'll give you one last thing to think about."

Charlie and Michael went out and got a gas can, filled it and walked back to the car. Once they were there, Charlie took the few gallons of gas he had brought and poured it into the tank. "Give it a try, Michael."

From inside the car, Michael turned the key and pumped the accelerator. After a few seconds, the engine came to life. *I can't believe it*, he thought. *I guess I should get that gauge fixed.*

There was a knock at the window. Michael rolled it down and looked up at Charlie. "Thanks a lot," Michael said. "I'm a little embarrassed, running out of gas and all. What do I owe you for the gas?"

"Oh, nothing. Nothing at all. Consider it a gift from Mr. Davis."

"Okay," Michael said, smiling. "I will. Tell him thanks for me."

"You know, I owe you one more piece of Mr. Davis's advice," Charlie said as he leaned down closer to Michael.

"Oh, yeah, what is it?" Michael was excited.

"You say that you want things to change for you and your family, right?"

"Yes, I really do."

"Mr. Davis says that the only way things are going to change for you is when you change. What are you going to change that will in turn change your life? If you keep on living like the way you are now, you will continue to produce the same life that you already have. That's the way it works."

Michael just stared out over the front of the car. His mind was racing. There were lots of things that he wanted to change. There were lots of things he knew he *needed* to change.

Charlie slapped the side of the car and said, "Okay, that's it for one day. You think on that, Michael. Then you feel free to stop on by sometime, and I'll tell you more about Mr. Davis's Pillars of Success." He handed Michael a business card that simply said "Charlie" on it, with a number.

"That's my workshop number—the best way to get a hold of me. Call the next time you're coming through."

"I will," Michael said. "I will." He smiled and put the car into drive and added, "Hop in and let me give you a lift to the gate."

"No thanks. I need the exercise, but I do have one last thing," Charlie said.

"What's that?"

"Get that gas gauge fixed," Charlie said with a grin.

"That you can be sure of," Michael said as he started to pull away.

Charlie stood and watched Michael drive away. *Nice boy,* he thought. *I hope he does come again. He has potential, but he also has some troubles and he needs the help.*

With that, Charlie turned and walked back in the direction of Twelve Pillars.

# 2
## Live a Life of Health

*"You should make sure that the outside of you is a good reflection of the inside of you."*

Michael knew that he would be passing by the estate where Charlie worked, so he called the number Charlie had given him and asked if he could stop by. It had been three weeks since he had run out of gas in front of Mr. Davis's estate. In hindsight, Michael considered it serendipitous, allowing him a chance to peek into a world he had once dreamed of and now seemed so far away. The fact that he had met Charlie, though, and Charlie's willingness to share the secrets of Mr. Davis's success was something that had started to reignite Michael's passion for excellence that had once burned bright.

Certainly life hadn't changed overnight, but he had been thinking about Charlie's words about changing himself and making himself better ever since that day Charlie challenged him. Michael realized that he had let himself go. He had stopped dreaming. He had become complacent. He was blaming circumstances rather than taking responsibility for himself and his situation.

But he was determined to change all of that. Since that day three weeks ago, Michael had written down a list of ten things about his life that he knew he could change if he applied himself. He looked at it each day and tried to work on at least one of them, just to make sure he was acting on what he knew was true.

They were small steps, but they were steps in the right direction. That was more than he had done for himself in years.

When Michael had called Charlie, Charlie said it would be great to see him again and invited him to swing by and chat. Michael told him what he had done since their last visit, and he was hoping Charlie would tell him some more about Mr. Davis. Charlie assured him he would be glad to.

Michael thought it was somewhat strange learning about Mr. Davis from Charlie, but he realized that a guy like him was hardly going to get a chance to spend much time with a rich, powerful, and busy man like Mr. Davis, so he was happy to take what he could get.

As he turned into the entrance, Michael saw that the gate was open, just as Charlie said it would be. He began down the driveway and could see that Charlie was out in the garden to the right of the house. There were gardens everywhere on the estate, and Michael guessed it must take Charlie a good twenty hours a week to keep them up, if not more. Each one seemed to be the perfect mix of colors and was impeccably maintained. Charlie was meticulous, that was for sure.

Michael pulled his car into one of the parking places next to the workshop and walked over toward Charlie. He looked toward the house, wondering if he would ever see any of the Davis family, perhaps even Mr. Davis himself. This day, however, he saw no one.

The sun was shining beautifully, and when Charlie looked up to greet Michael, he held his gloved hand up to shield the sun.

"Hello, Michael. Good to see you again."

"Great to see you, too, Charlie."

Charlie motioned to the garden. "You don't mind if I keep on weeding and pruning while we talk, do you?"

"No, not at all," Michael replied.
"I'm glad you called to stop by. You were coming through anyway?"

"Yes, I have an appointment this afternoon, but I wanted to drop by if you were around."

"Well, I am certainly around. What's on your mind?"

"I have been thinking about our last conversation, quite a bit actually."

"You have?" Charlie asked, as he knelt back down to work on the flowers he had been tending to. "What have you been thinking?"

"Just about needing to change my life and work on myself. I had given up and just accepted mediocrity. I realized that I want more for my life. I mean, seeing Mr. Davis's house and all, it gave me a little vision of what I could become—not that I will ever become as rich or successful as Mr. Davis—but it showed me that more is possible. Does that make sense?"

"It certainly does, Michael. Seeing what others have accomplished can provide you with a positive ambition of your own."

"This may seem strange," Michael said, "but I am wondering if you wouldn't mind telling me the other eleven 'Pillars of Success' as you—uh, as Mr. Davis—puts it. I was thinking that from time to time, maybe you and I could get together and you could tell me more about Mr. Davis and how he got to be where he is in life."

"I think that would be fantastic, Michael. I get the feeling that you are ready to grow some."

"I sure am. I guess it may be desperation. I am really just tired of living like I am. I need more, and I figure knowing someone who knows how a person can become so successful is as good a route as any."

"It is a great route, Michael. So, what do you want to know?"

"Well, why not just tell me the next couple of Pillars? I am assuming you know them all, right? Sort of like the Ten Commandments?" He said this with a slight chuckle.

"Well, they aren't quite the Ten Commandments, Michael, but they are important nonetheless, and, yes, I know them—quite well."

"I have thirty minutes. Next time, I'll schedule more time if you can do it. But maybe you could tell me the next two today, and I can begin working on them."

"Did you work on the first one yet? That's important because you have to apply what you learn."

"I did apply it. I made a list of things I can control and change in my life, and I have taken a couple of small steps toward improving."

"Very good, Michael. I'll be glad to tell you the next two then." Charlie saw a small weed, and he pulled it quickly from the ground and tossed it to a pile he had been building on since earlier that morning.

"Pillar number two is Total Well-Being. Mr. Davis believes in what he calls 'three-dimensional health.' "

"What's that?"

"Well, when you say 'health' to most people, they think of your physical well-being, but Mr. Davis thinks of it as more than that. He thinks that a person is made up of three parts: the body, the soul, and the spirit. Three dimensions."

"Okay, I could guess, but can you explain it a bit more than that?"

"Sure. We have our bodies, that's obvious. But we also have our soul, which is basically our intellect and our emotions, also our will; and then we have our spirit. That is the part of us that transcends this world. It is the part of us that is designed to be eternal. The fact is that most people pick one of those and work exclusively on that area. Mr. Davis thinks we need to work on each area because they are interdependent."

"What do you mean, 'They pick one area and work on it?' "

"You have some people who work on their physical health. Now, don't get me wrong. We need to work on ourselves because for so many people that is an area they neglect. Have you ever noticed that some people take better care of their pets than they do themselves? Their animals can run like the wind, but they can barely make it up a flight of stairs. Those who take care of their physical health many times neglect the other two areas.

"Other people are all about the intellect and forget their bodies or spirits. And then there are people who are so spiritual they are no earthly good. Mr. Davis believes that you function best when you live in balance. Are you in balance, Michael?"

Michael looked down at his forty-year-old stomach. *Not bad,* he thought. "Well, I am in pretty good shape. I could work out a bit more."

"What about your intellect, your emotions, and your spiritual life?" Charlie pressed.

"I admit, I don't read much. I watch television when I have free time."

"That won't do you much good," Charlie broke in.

Michael continued. "As for my spiritual life..." He just let it go because he didn't know how to answer.

"Cat got your tongue?" Charlie kidded, looking up.

"No, I just don't do much with that."

"Well, it is very important. The most important. Mr. Davis says that it is like a three-layered onion. You peel each layer back until you get to the core. The spiritual is at the core, and it is the most important. Then the second layer is the soul, and the outer layer is the physical—the body. Each part rests on the one below it, and it is only as strong as the layer below. Make sense?"

"Yeah, I guess so. So where do I start?"

"You can start by going back to your roots. Did you grow up with any spiritual influence?"

"Yes, sure did. Went to church every week."

"There you go. Start there. Read good material that will help you reflect on your spiritual life. That's a good place to start. What about the physical?"

"I don't get much time to exercise."

"You need to start. Even if it is just a half-hour a day. You're married, right?"

"Yes, I sure am."

"Ask your wife to go on a nightly walk for a half-hour. She'll love it and you'll get some exercise. The idea is to get started. Mr. Davis always says that we should take good care of our body because it is the only place we have to live."

"That's a good idea."

"Yes, Michael, you should make sure that the outside of you is a good reflection of the inside of you. If you focus on improving all of these three areas—the body, soul, and spirit—you will see that each one will get stronger, and the stronger they get, the stronger they will make the others. It all ties together. That's Pillar Two."

"Got it." Michael looked at his watch and realized he only had another 10 minutes or so. He wished he had given himself more time. "What is number three?"

# 3
## The Gift of Relationships

*"Time, effort, and imagination must be summoned constantly to keep any relationship flourishing and growing."*

"Ah, yes. The third Pillar of Success. I am glad you asked because this is the perfect setting for discussing this. The third Pillar of Success is to make the most of the Gift of Relationships."

"The *Gift of Relationships*? What does that mean?"

"Mr. Davis likes to say that the greatest gift the Grand Designer gives is the gift of other people. Yes, relationships can be hard, but they are also what the joy of life is made of."

"They can be hard, all right," Michael said.

"Michael, relationships represent the most beautiful highs of life as well as some of the most tormented lows of life. It is all what you make of them. That is why it is good that we are discussing it now… and here."

Michael looked around him and saw nothing but flowers, dirt, yard tools, and a bag of fertilizer. "Here and now? I don't get it."

"Mr. Davis says, 'Your family and your love must be cultivated like a garden. Time, effort, and imagination must be summoned constantly to keep any relationship flourishing and growing.' " He paused, looked down around him, and then continued. "Michael, tell me about your family."

"You mean, like my whole family, or my family as in my wife and kids?"

"Tell me about them all."

"Well, let's see. My mom and dad are both dead. My dad was a normal guy. Worked hard. Didn't make much money. Kind of a boring life. Mom was great, but simple. She didn't want for much or push dad much. It was basically a simple life growing up. No excitement or drama either way. I always kind of hoped I would grow up and get much more out of life."

"And your siblings?"

"One sister. She and her husband have two kids. They live in Denver. I don't talk to them much. No hard feelings, but we were never close and we have just drifted away over the years. We talk on the phone on the holidays. That's about it."

"And your wife and children?"

"Yes, I have a wife, Amy, and two kids. Mike, Jr., is eleven and Jennifer is nine. They are great."

"And is the relationship *great*?"

"You ask too many questions," Michael deadpanned. "No, the relationship isn't great. It used to be. Amy and I were so in love. We had dreams. We were excited to set out on our own. And then we just fell into life. Work was hard, we had kids, we let things slip, and we woke up one day wondering who the other person was."

"I see. The weeds crept in."

"The weeds?"

"Yes, like a garden. The weeds crept in. Michael, this is why it is good to be here, in the garden. You see, relationships are the backbone of our existence. We need to cultivate them as best we can. When you are on your deathbed, you want your family there with you, sending you on your journey. That is the sign of an excellent life. You can gain every possession in the world, but if you lose your relationships, what good has your life been? No, instead, you must tend to your relationships. Like this garden."

"I'm listening."

"Michael, how do you like my garden?"

"It's beautiful. Mr. Davis is lucky to have you take such good care of it."

"Yes, it is beautiful, if I do say so myself," Charlie said with a grin. "But it didn't get that way by itself. No. I *made* it that way. This plot of ground we are standing on could be one of two things: the beautiful thing that it is or a collection of weeds. Maybe three, if you count completely barren. Left to itself, it would be weeds. But with some care and work, with a little imagination thrown in for good measure, it has become something beautiful. And your relationships can, too."

"So how do I do that?"

"Do you *want* to do that?" Charlie prodded.

Michael didn't answer right away but then said, "Yes, of course I do."

"That doesn't sound too convincing."

"I do. It's just…"

"It's just what?"

"It's just hard."

"Of course, it's hard, Michael. Life is hard. Success is hard. If you want easy, you can have it, but you won't get much of anything else, especially not anything of value. That which is valuable is hard to get. That is why so few go for it. Do you think that tending to these gardens is easy? No. But they sure look great when you get them done. And they provide enjoyment. And the neat thing is that once you get them up and running, then the maintenance is easier to keep them going. If you let them get bad, boy, watch out. Lots of work then."

"Tell me about it," Michael said, somewhat dejected.

"Don't despair, Michael, you can still pull it out. Let's give you a plan for tending to that garden you have at home. Remember that I said that it takes time, effort, and imagination?"

"Yes."

"Well, let's think through how you can begin to apply that to your marriage. And a brief parenthetical statement here—these principles work for any relationship. They work for work relationships, people at your church, your friends, anything. Time, effort, and imagination."

"Okay, what do I do?"

"Let's start with time. Spend more time with Amy. Spend more time with the kids. Spend more time with your friends. Remember, life is always about the relationships, and the way to build relationships is by giving them time."

"I always thought it was quality time, not quantity time," Michael quipped.

"I would like to see the person who said that. Their spouse probably wasn't happy."

Michael laughed, "Probably not."

"It is *both*, Michael. You need to spend time with someone if you want a relationship with them. And the time you spend must be quality. The more and the better the time, the better the relationship. If you are like most young people today, you are running around like the proverbial chicken with its head cut off, never spending time with that wife of yours—or the kids. They need you to be there, Michael."

"But it is hard with work and other responsibilities," Michael argued, albeit pathetically.

"That is why we say effort is needed. People are hard. You are hard to be around. I am hard to be around. It is a fact of life. People aren't perfect. That makes it hard to deal with them. But we all need people, especially if you want to be successful. You cannot succeed by yourself. It is hard to find a rich hermit."

Again, Michael chuckled. "That it is, I suppose."

"It takes effort to make the time. It takes effort to put up with another person's faults. It takes plain-old effort!"

Michael checked his watch. "Okay, got it, but I have to get going. What about imagination?"

"Imagination just means that you have to see with your imagination what the relationship *could* be. Use your imagination to take Amy out for a date like you used to. Use your imagination to plan a fantastic vacation for your family. Use the creativity that you use on the job to be successful in your family."

"I guess I have been neglecting it lately."

"And you have the weeds to show for it. Now, you have to go. But here is your assignment: The next time you come back here, I want to hear about this garden you are growing through time, effort, and imagination."

"I may have to pull a few weeds first," Michael said.

"That's okay. Speak to your wife. Ask for forgiveness. Tell her what you want to do. Pull those weeds, and plant some beautiful flowers so they may bloom."

Michael stuck his hand out, and Charlie took it. They shook hands firmly as Michael looked Charlie in the eyes. "Thanks, Charlie. I appreciate it."

"My pleasure, Michael."

"I gotta go."

"No problem. I will see you the next time. Just call me when you are going to be near again. I enjoy our conversations."

"I do, too," Michael assured him. "I will call soon."

"Great."

With that, Charlie went back to his garden, and Michael went off to develop his own garden.

# 4
# Achieve Your Goals

*"The major reason for setting a goal is for what it makes of you to accomplish it."*

Mack's Diner is exactly the kind of place you would expect a maintenance man to hang out in—small place next to the road, gravel parking lot with pickup trucks populating it, the smell of fried food hitting you while you are still 10 feet from the front door—in other words, *perfect*.

It had been about four weeks since Michael and Charlie had last met, so Michael called Charlie to arrange getting together. Charlie had to run some errands and knew a great little diner that would be in the middle for both of them, and that is how Michael had come to make his first trip to Mack's.

When Michael walked through the door, he smelled one of his favorite smells—bacon! A true hole-in-the-wall diner. He saw Charlie talking with some other old-timers in the back corner, all wearing the ubiquitous uniform of estate maintenance men everywhere—coveralls.

When Charlie saw Michael come through the door, he excused himself from the others and met Michael halfway into the diner, walking somewhat slowly.

"Hey, Michael, great to see you. You look good."

"You do, too, Charlie. But you're walking a little slow. Everything okay?"

"Just age. Us old folks take a while to get places. You'll see."

"Okay, just checking on you."

"Well, let's grab this table right here," Charlie said, pointing at an empty table that looked just like you would expect a table to look in an old diner—silver legs, Formica top, plastic-covered chairs.

The two men took their seats as a waitress came over and asked if they would like coffee. "Absolutely," Charlie said. "Michael?"

"Yes, please."

"I'll be right back," she cheerfully said.

"Well, she's in a happy mood," Michael noticed.

"That's Sue. She's always happy, it seems. Great attitude."

"So, Charlie, how long have you worked at Twelve Pillars anyway?"

"Since the very first day. Even while it was being built, actually. I've been there for the whole thing."

"So what did you do before that?"

"I was in business. I did okay for myself. When I retired, I realized I love to take care of things and fix things, do gardening and the like, so that is what I spend my days doing now." Charlie changed gears. "So, how is Amy?"

"Oh, she's good. Really good, actually. That is the main reason I wanted to get together with you—to tell you about how things have gone since you taught me about gardens."

"Well, do tell," Charlie prodded.

"It's simple, really. I just went home and started thinking about my relationship with Amy like I would if I were planting or maintaining a garden. Not that I am Mr. Expert Gardener or anything, but the metaphor really worked for me. It gave me something to use as an example. The main thing is that I just started putting more time into the relationship."

"How so?"

Sue the waitress arrived with their coffee, and Michael waited for her to set it down.

"Anything to eat today?

"Not for me," Charlie said.

"Just coffee for me. Thanks."

"Okay," she smiled.

And off went the perpetually happy Sue.

"Back to the matter at hand," Michael said with a smile. "To answer your question, I started making time, first and foremost, by doing a night each week where I get a babysitter and we go out for something Amy wants to do. Her choice of restaurant, movie, bookstore—whatever. She loves it. It has been like a ray of sunshine on a flower!"

"That's great," Charlie said. "I am so glad for you. You will have to keep me posted as it progresses. Just remember that once a flower blooms, it still needs water and sun to keep it from wilting. The work isn't over when the color comes out."

"I'll remember that."

"So what else is new, Michael? How is work and the rest of your life?"

"Life is pretty good. As I've said before, my major challenge is work. I just wish I was further along in my career. I feel like I am not living up to my potential."

"Hmmm.... What are your goals for your career?" Charlie asked. "Goals? That may be my problem. I guess I don't have any goals."

"That may be why you are achieving what you are achieving then."

"I think you may be right. You know, I always hear about goal-setting and what not, but I have never done it. I suppose you have heard Mr. Davis talk about goal-setting, huh?"

"That I have. It is one of his favorite subjects."

"What does he say? He must know a lot about goals to live in a place like he does."

"Oh, that he does, Michael. That he does."

"Okay, shoot then."

"It's pretty simple stuff."

"I'm ready."

"Here it goes: Write it down."

"I don't have a pen."

Charlie laughed. "No, that's the advice: Write it down. Write your goal down."

Michael laughed, too. "Oh, I thought you meant... never mind. Okay, so write my goals down. That's it?"

"That's it. I told you it was simple."

"So what good does that do?"

"Think about it, Michael. It does two things. First, in order to write it down, it means you have to have a goal in the first place, which, at this point, would be a great start for you. Secondly, there is a power in writing your goal down. It brings it into reality. One of the best things you can do is to write down one hundred things you want to accomplish before you die. Just the process of deciding what they are is powerful, but when you get them written down, watch out, because now you are likely to achieve them."

"Why is that?"

"Because now your mind is cognitively aware of them. Your mind then gets to work achieving them. That should be your first goal: to write down your one hundred goals."

"All right, I'll do that. It can't hurt."

"Here is something else Mr. Davis teaches that is important, Michael. He says that the major reason for setting a goal is for what it makes of you to accomplish it. What it makes of you will always be the far greater value than the goal you achieve. Mr. Davis always says, 'Make a million dollars, not for the million dollars, but for what you will have to become to make a million dollars.' That's pretty good advice."

"So the real goal is to let the goal make me a better person?"
"That's exactly it, Michael."

"Hey, I think I'm getting this success thing."

"I think you are. It is exciting, isn't it?"

"It sure is. I feel like I'm coming alive just hearing and talking about it, even though I haven't changed much yet."

"Yes, the power of change is exciting. You have a great future ahead of you."

"Yeah, I just wish I was already there."

"Well, as Mr. Davis also says frequently, 'You cannot change your destination overnight, but you can change your direction overnight.' "

"Yeah, I know that I can't become what I want overnight. I guess that's what is so frustrating. I feel like I have wasted so many years, and now I will have to take a long road to be successful. I just don't know where to start."

"Start by changing your direction. You are where you are, but you don't have to stay there. Choose where you want to go, and then build out your plan for getting there."

"How do I do that?"

"That is where goals come in. Let's say, for example, that you want to have a certain life, a certain income, or job, in ten years. Would you be able to dream something big for yourself to achieve in ten years?"

"Sure."

"Okay, then that is your long-range goal. Or you could make your long-range goal five years. Whatever is out there in the future that you want to achieve. Then you choose somewhere in the middle for your midrange goal, say five years on a ten-year goal. And then a short-range goal for a year or two out. You might even have what Mr. Davis calls 'micro-goals' that are just months out. The key is that each one leads you to the final goal."

"Give me an example," Michael said.

"For example, let's assume that you wanted to be able to open your own business in five years. Maybe you need to save $50,000 to do it right. You may have a few goals that all work together. You may have to save the $50,000 and you may have to learn certain skills. Then you break it down. For the financial, you would have to save about $850 a month and never touch it. At the end, you would have $50,000. And that doesn't even take into consideration that you would probably keep it in a mutual fund that would pay you interest or earn a return that would help you get to $50,000 sooner. A three-year goal would be to have $25,000, and a one-year goal would be to save $10,000."

"How would I ever do that?" Michael asked, looking and sounding astonished.

"I never said it was going to be easy, but you could do it. You could cut spending, get a second job, sell some things.... It can be done.

And then for the skills you would be learning, do the same thing: Set the goal and work backward. It is simple really."

"Well, I better get to it in a hurry, that's for sure."

"Just decide what you want to do and then get started. That is one of the most powerful lessons in life."

# 5
# The Proper Use of Time

---

*"Every day has many opportunities, but only one best opportunity."*

"Refill?" Sue asked, beaming.

"Sure, I'll take another cup," Charlie said.

"I will, too," Michael said.

Sue poured each man a cup and then hurried away.

"I don't know, Charlie. I just don't have the time now to get going in the right direction. I am swamped with work, home, a wife, and kids....

I just don't know where I would fit a goal in."

"These words have come from Mr. Davis's mouth on more than one occasion: 'We must all suffer from one of two pains: the pain of discipline or the pain of regret. The difference is discipline weighs ounces while regret weighs tons.' Very important words are those, Michael."

"I guess I don't get it."

"Well, think about your deathbed, Michael. There are certain things—things you have yet to do, but long to do—that if you don't achieve them during your lifetime, you will have deep regrets. There is one certainty, and that is that the end of your life will come, and sooner than you want. I am an old man now, and I am amazed by how fast life has gone by. For me, it is almost over. Luckily, I have lived well. I have done almost everything I desired. Yet, so many men and women never even let themselves dream, and those who do, most of them never overcome their fear and strive for their dream. Then, one day, they wake up on their deathbed and there is nothing—not one single thing—that they can do about it. Their bodies are frail, weak, and unwilling. Then they suffer from the crushing weight of the pain of regret.

"You see," Charlie continued, "days are expensive. When you spend a day, you have one less day to spend. So make sure you spend each one wisely."

"How do you know if you are spending your day wisely?" Michael asked.

"Mr. Davis would tell you that your day is being spent wisely if it is being spent in the best way possible. Every day has many opportunities, but only one best opportunity. Your best opportunities are those that align with your overall goals and should be what you spend your time on. Would that be how you describe your days, Michael?"

"No, my days are spent getting by. Making sure I get paid so I can pay the bills."

"And that is exactly the time-management trap that most people get into. They spend their time on the urgent rather than the important. The urgent is a tyrant of a master that enslaves you if you let it. It is better to be the master of time rather than vice-versa. It is important to be the designer of our lives.

"Michael, if you don't design your own life plan, chances are you will fall into someone else's plan. And guess what they have planned for you?"

"What?"

"Not much," Charlie said with a broad grin on his face.

"That's for sure," Michael said with a subtle laugh.

"Yes, Michael, something will master and something will serve. Either you run the day or the day runs you. Either you control your time or it controls you. Take your pick."

Just then, Michael's pager on his cell phone went off. He looked at it and then said, "Well, the urgent is calling. I have to get going." He started to stand and put his coat on.

"Nothing too urgent, I hope."

"No, but I do have to run. Work stuff." Michael looked sincerely at Charlie. "I really appreciate you taking the time to teach me this stuff, Charlie. You have sure gleaned a lot from old Mr. Davis. It is great of you to pass it on to me. Thanks."

Charlie stood and shook Michael's hand. "It is my pleasure, Michael. I enjoy it very much. That is what life is about—us old folks helping you young whippersnappers."

They both chuckled. "Now, don't you go so long between visits, young man. You give me a call and swing by the house sooner rather than later, okay?"

"I sure will," Michael said as he walked toward the door, looking back over his shoulder. "Real soon, I promise."

The door swung closed, and Michael was on his way to put out some unimportant fire.

# 6
# Surround Yourself with the Best People

*"Don't join an easy crowd; you won't grow. Go where the expectations and the demands to perform are high."*

It had been three weeks since Michael and Charlie met at the diner, and Michael wanted to visit so he could share his achievement. When he got to Twelve Pillars, he parked near the workshop and walked around to the back of the house by the pool like Charlie had told him to. There was old Charlie, standing next to the pool in a ray of sunlight, dressed in his coveralls, holding a pool cleaning net.

"Hey, Charlie," Michael yelled from across the yard.

"Well, hello there, Michael. You are a few minutes early. Just in time to help me clean the pool!"

"Oh, you don't want me doing any kind of labor. I might break the pool."

By now Michael was walking around the end of the pool. It looked pretty clean to him.

"That's okay. I am almost done anyway. I am just getting the last few leaves from the bottom. Then I'll add a few chemicals and it will be good to go."

"Well, it looks pretty good to me," Michael said.

"I do my best. So, how are things?"
"Pretty good. I have good news."

"Good news is always good news," Charlie said.

"Actually, two pieces of good news. One, Amy and I are doing even better—tending to the garden, you know. And secondly, I wrote down my one hundred goals in life. Then I put them into the different categories, long term, etc. It was pretty fun doing that."

"I'll bet. It is always fun to dream. And very motivating as well."

"Yeah, especially about my family, my career, my income, and places I want to travel. It was really enlightening to do it."

"How long did it take?" Charlie asked.

"Oh, not long at all. Maybe an hour and a half."

"Very good. So where is your top place to visit?"

"Oh, that was easy—Italy. I have always wanted to go there. All the history, the architecture, the art, the culture, the food... I can't wait. But what was most amazing—and you said this would happen—is that when I wrote it down, my mind started thinking about how to make it happen. Once I crystallized the goal, my mind started trying to make it a reality."

"That's the way it works. Congratulations, Michael!"

"Thanks. I owe it to Mr. Davis's Pillars of Success—via you, of course."

"Yes, he knows a thing or two about success," Charlie said while continuing to stir the net through the water. Every few strokes, he would pull the net out and shake the contents into a bin he had by him.

"So, here I am, ready for the next Pillars of Success. Can you teach them to me?"

"I would be happy to." Charlie wedged the net to the bottom of the pool, and then placed his hands on the top of the pole and his chin on his hands, resting it there while thinking. "Let's see.... How about this one: Surround yourself with the best."

"Okay.... What does that mean? Buy expensive things?"

"No, not the best things. The best people. Surround yourself with winners, successful people who exhibit and live consistent to values and skills you want to acquire and develop. You see, the people in your life have an amazing power to influence your destiny. They have a deep affect on you. Mr. Davis says that you must constantly ask yourself these questions: Who am I around? What effect are they having on me? What have they got me reading? What have they got me saying? Where do they have me going? What do they have me thinking? And, most importantly, what do they have me becoming? Then ask yourself the big question: Is that okay?"

"So you are talking about my friends?"

"Your friends, your spouse, your co-workers, and your family. *All* of the people we surround ourselves with. It is important to ask how they affect us. Since you mentioned your friends, let's start there."

"Okay, what do you mean?"

"Well, they have a tremendous affect on you. Let's take a look at them. Tell me about your three closest friends."

"That's easy because we just went out last Friday. There is John, Clark, and Tom. We have been friends since the third grade. We go out almost every single Friday night."

"And what do they do for a living? What do they do for fun? What are they like?" Charlie asked.

"Let's see. John is in retail. He was going to college, but didn't like the structure so he dropped out."

"Does he like his current job better than he did the structure?"

"Good point. No, he hates his job. But he's been there for over a decade and makes enough to cover his expenses. Kind of hard to quit now."

"In the corporate world, they call that 'golden handcuffs,' yet I have a hard time using that term for the salary he probably makes. Tell me about Clark."

"Clark. Well, he makes John look good. At least John has a job. Clark has been unemployed for about two years. Just can't find anything he likes or that pays what he wants to make."

"I see," said Charlie, sounding unimpressed. "And Tom?"

"Tom is probably my best friend. We have been since we met. We like the same things, enjoy hobbies together, etc. But it can be hard at times because he has quite a temper."

"A temper?"

"Yeah, he can blow his stack at the drop of a hat."

"Yes, I see. Well, I think that you may need to make some adjustments in your friendships."

"You mean give up my friends?"

"I wouldn't say that yet, but what I am saying is that when you ask yourself the question, 'What effect do my friends have on me?' you've got to be *willing* to take an honest look at what kind of influence they currently have on you. In other words, are they helping you grow in the direction you want? What if keeping your associations the same, not making room for expanding any new associations, or limiting your current relationships meant the difference in becoming what you want and achieving the life of your dreams for you and your family?"

"Do you really think my friends are holding me back?"

"Well, let's take a look at it. When we go back to the question I asked before, 'What effect are they having on me?' To be more specific on this, you have to ask, 'Where do they have me going? What are we spending our time doing?' If you spend every Friday night out drinking with your friends, griping about how you hate your jobs, bosses, and how broke you all are, what kind of influence is that? When you leave, do you feel inspired to be more and do more, to pursue your goals with a greater passion, or does it leave you feeling negative, dreading the next workday when you have to get up to spend another day at the office with that boss you're not too fond of anyway? Influence is so subtle; it's like a little nudge, and each time you get together, there is one more nudge in the wrong direction, toward the wrong attitudes down the path you don't want to be on. Michael, I know this is a touchy subject, and so many of us have friends who are nice people, often who intend well, but if the effect they have on us is negative, then it is up to us to make those tough choices in an effort to protect ourselves from the wrong influences."

Michael sat for a moment, just staring at Charlie.

"Michael?"

Finally Michael snapped to. "I guess I had never thought of it that way before. I had never given thought to how they were and how that may have affected me."

"Most people don't, Michael, so don't feel badly, but they are simple questions that can have a powerful influence on how your life turns out. Let me teach you one of Mr. Davis's principles that is very effective at helping people decide about their relationships. You see, every relationship you have is an association, and each association has either a positive, neutral, or negative effect on you. So a person who wants to achieve success has to constantly make a determination about what kind of relationship it is and how to approach that relationship."

"How do you do that?" Michael asked.

"It is simple, really. You place every person you meet into one of three categories: disassociation, limited association, and expanded association. You simply ask yourself whether each person is someone you should stop associating, limit your association with, or expand your association."

"So I should do that with my friends?"

"That is for you to decide, Michael. I would certainly say that given their life situations and such, that you don't want to expand your association with them. You are going in opposite directions. You then have to decide if you should limit your association with them or even disassociate with them."

"How do I decide that?"

"Let me put it this way, Michael. One of the things I have to do to keep this pool clean is to keep the pH levels balanced by adding the right chemicals in the right amounts. Now, if I add too much of one chemical, the water might look good on the surface, but you won't be able to swim in it because it will burn your eyes. If I don't add enough of a chemical, then the water starts to produce algae and turns green or, worse yet, brown. Relationships and associations are the same way. Ask yourself what amount of time with each person will challenge you to become the kind of person you want. If the answer is eliminating the time you spend, then you need to consider disassociating with them. Michael, life is rarely simple, and at times we are faced with difficult decisions that, if we avoid, can cost us dearly in the future."

"But they have been my friends for decades!" Michael argued.

"Are they friends of convenience?" Charlie asked.

"Friends of convenience? I don't get it."

"I wonder if they aren't your friends because it was easier to continue the relationship with them than it was to pursue new relationships."

Again, silence from Michael. Charlie was really pushing buttons now.

Charlie continued. "All along the path of life, you had points where you could have chosen to develop new relationships. You still can. Successful people look for relationships with other successful people who will push them, challenge them, and encourage them to become better."

"So how do you find people like that?"

"I am glad you asked because it reminds me of something Mr. Davis says all of the time. He says, 'To attract attractive people you must be attractive. To attract powerful people, you must be powerful. To attract committed people, you must be committed. Instead of going to work on them, go to work on yourself. If you become, you can attract.'"

"So it goes back to personal development?"

"By golly, I think you are getting it," Charlie said with a beaming smile.

"But no attractive, successful people are going to want to hang around with me."

"You are right in one sense. The world's richest man won't want to spend his vacation with you based on how you are now, but you can begin to expand your relationships over time to include people you admire. The more successful you become, the more successful the people you will be able to be in relationship with. Spend some time thinking about successful people you know or work with. Chances are that the reason they don't give you the time of day now is because they think you are stuck or have no desire to improve. If you showed some ambition, they would probably be happy to begin to let you into their world."

"Do you think so?"

"I do. I have seen it all of my life. Mr. Davis regularly takes a liking to young, up-and-coming businesspeople. They aren't at his level yet, but he likes that they want to be. That gives him the impetus to spend time with them and invest his life into theirs."

Hmmmm.... Michael was deep in thought about the people he admired and wished he could spend time with.

Charlie interrupted his thought. "And do you know what happens when you begin to hang around and associate with more successful people?"

"What?"

"A few things. First of all, you open yourself up to all sorts of new knowledge. Knowledge about how the world works, how business works, how to better your relationships. Second, you open yourself up to a vast new network. Their friends become your friends. Soon, your whole business and sphere of influence has changed for the better. And lastly, and most importantly, your attitude changes. And ninety-nine percent of life is attitude, Michael."

"And my friends determine my attitude?"

"It isn't that they determine your attitude—you determine your attitude—but it is like Mr. Davis always says, 'Attitude is greatly shaped by influence and association.' "
"What does he mean by that?" Michael asked.

"It is simple, really. Who you hang around with will be a major determining *factor* in what your attitude becomes. Think about it. You spend time with them and share your life with them. And when you interact with them, all of your attitudes intermingle and shape one another. If the people you spend time with don't have attitudes that are positive, they will rub off on you and keep you from becoming all that you can be."

"So, I can't have a positive attitude if I spend time with my old friends?"

"Let's put it this way: two things to think about. First, I have never seen anyone who was successful who spent much time with people who have bad attitudes. They surround themselves with winners, optimists, and people with positive attitudes. And secondly, everything you have done up until now and everybody you have associated with has added up to your current situation. In other words, maybe if you changed your associations, the results in your life and career would change."

Michael knew in his heart that Charlie was right, but he didn't want him to be.

Charlie spoke again. "Michael, leaving people behind is hard, I know. I have had to do it myself. But I like to think of it this way: Life is a long journey, and we meet people all along the way. Some of those people will go the whole journey with us. Some will only take portions of the journey with us. Some will join us for a long time. Others will come and go. Now, imagine if you were on a trip and someone started out with you, but wasn't much help. Would you want them to continue on the journey with you? Of course not. We have the freedom—and responsibility—to determine who we associate with, and that will have a big impact on how well our journey goes."

"Boy, Charlie, I feel like I am learning so much. I have never heard these things before, and I admit they are not easy words to hear, but they make sense. I just wish I had learned these lessons before. Where has Mr. Davis been my whole life?" At this last part, Michael was smiling.

"Oh, Mr. Davis has been around, but perhaps you just weren't ready."

"Ready?"

"Yes, ready. Mr. Davis says that when the student is ready, the teacher will appear. Now you are ready. Your car stopped here one day, and I was available to teach you Mr. Davis's Twelve Pillars of Success."

"Well, I am ready to learn now, that's for sure!"

# 7
# Be a Lifelong Learner

*"Formal education will make you a living.
Self-education will make you a fortune."*

"That's great, Michael. Great." Charlie, who had been methodically taking leaves and small debris out of the pool, pulled the long pole out and placed it down on a specially made rack designed to hold it. Next to him was a bucket with small plastic bottles holding pool chemicals. He began to measure out the chemicals and pour them into the pool as he continued. "You know, Mr. Davis's next Pillar of Success is about learning. So it is fortuitous that we have stumbled onto the topic."

"Cool. Tell me what it is."

"Well, it is this: A successful person is always a lifelong learner."

"A lifelong learner?"

"Yes. How many people do you know who graduated high school or college and then figured they knew everything they needed to know to live life?" He didn't wait for an answer. "Too many!"

"But I learned lots of good things in college."

"It isn't that you don't learn good things in college—you do—it is just that it isn't what will make you successful in life. Here is what Mr. Davis says: 'Formal education will make you a living. Self-education will make you a fortune.' You can graduate from your formal education—and the masses do—but the great writer Thoreau said that the masses 'lead lives of quiet desperation and go to the grave with the song still in them.' And that, it seems, is exactly where you are right now."

"Charlie, quoting Henry David Thoreau—I'm impressed!" Michael joked.

"Well, this old boy will surprise you from time to time, young man," Charlie said while looking at a bottle of chemicals, being ever so careful to get just the right amount. "The point is that if you want to succeed in this life, formal education isn't the end-all. Self-education is the key."

"Okay, so what do you mean by self-education?"

"Self-education is what you teach yourself. It is what you learn along the way so that you are constantly improving and growing. Most people don't continue to learn or grow, so the very fact that you are doing so means you are well on your way to improving your life."

"I am not sure I am already doing it."

"Of course, you are. You are here, aren't you? That is self-education. You can learn as much about success from an old man putting chemicals in the pool as you can in the fanciest college classroom. What I am teaching you is invaluable—if you apply it."

"You know, I believe you. A few years ago I would have said you were off your rocker, but now, after struggling so long, I believe you."

"Michael, Mr. Davis says, 'If someone is going down the wrong path, he doesn't need motivation to speed him up. He needs education to turn him around. Learning is the beginning of wealth. Learning is the beginning of health. Learning is the beginning of spirituality. Searching and learning are where the miracle process all begins.' Well, that education is self-education. Most of life is lived after your formal education. That means the rest is up to you. The state makes you go to school through twelfth grade, then most people choose to go through college, but the truly successful decide to learn for the rest of their lives."

"So, how do they do that?"

"There are a few mainstays to learning that anyone can use to improve their lives. The first is to read books. The second is to learn from successful people by observation. And the third is to constantly reflect on your own experiences and learn what went right and what went wrong."

"Well, I know that the book thing isn't going to work."

Charlie looked up at Michael in disbelief. "The 'book thing?' " he asked.

"Yeah, you know, reading books. I know myself well enough to know that I am not going to be reading any books anytime soon."

"You are kidding me, right?"

"No. I haven't read a book in years."

"Well, there you go—that right there is a significant part of the problem."

"Not reading books?"

"Certainly." Charlie put the chemicals down and motioned for Michael to join him sitting in a couple of chairs at poolside. "Here, sit down. This is a serious point, Michael."

They both sat down and Michael asked, "What's the big deal about books? It seems like everybody writes a book. It's just a big money-making scam. What can you learn from a book anyway—and besides that, books cost so much money. When you go to the bookstore, some of those books are twenty or thirty bucks."

Charlie knew this was going to be a tough sell. "Michael, if I may be blunt, books have been, are, and will continue to be one of the greatest learning tools in human history. As for the cost, Mr. Davis, a man who has been extraordinarily successful, always says that, 'It isn't what the book costs. It's what it will cost you if you don't read it.'"

"How will it cost me if I don't read it?" Michael asked.

"It will cost you in many ways. In fact, I believe that your attitude toward books has already cost you a decade or two of your life. You see, when we read books, we open ourselves to vast new worlds to explore and understand. Have you ever wanted to sit down and have dinner with great leaders or famous thinkers? You can when you read their books. You open yourself to new ideas, and new ideas are the seeds that grow in our hearts and minds, and when applied, become our achievements and successes. Michael, how will you ever grow and expand if you aren't consistently and proactively pursuing knowledge and ideas that will move your life forward?"

"Uh, I guess I had never thought of it that way."

"From now on, you must think of it that way."

"So Mr. Davis is a big reader, huh?"

"That he is. Almost a book a week for forty years. And that is where he gets his wisdom. Before you leave, I will give you a copy of a book list that he has written. I have a few copies of it in my workshop."

"I don't know…"

"Michael, I insist. You can set a goal of reading one of the books before we meet again. In fact, I hate to be harsh, but I won't schedule the meeting until you have read one of the books."

"That does seem harsh."

"Michael, I do it with a good heart. I so believe in reading that I do not believe you can move forward without it."

"Really?"

"Absolutely," Charlie said with conviction. "You must also learn from people who are succeeding—that is the idea of association we talked about earlier—and we all must learn from ourselves as we live life making mistakes and achieving victories."

"Well, I have learned so much from Mr. Davis—and you, Charlie— that I am willing to try anything that you suggest. And, I imagine that I can always go down to my library and pick up most of the books."

"I'll bet you can."

Charlie stood up. "Listen, I know that you probably have things to do and I have to finish up with this pool and then get about running some errands, so let's get up to the workshop so I can dig up one of those sheets with Mr. Davis's recommended books on it."

Michael stood up as well and began to turn toward the direction of the workshop. "Okay, that would be great. I *promise* I will read one before I get back to you. It may take me a while, though."

Charlie took the lead and began walking in front of Michael toward the workshop. "That is quite alright. We will get together when you are done with it. I am sure you will enjoy it because you are in a mode of growth right now. You will soak it in like water on the desert floor."

As they walked, Michael noticed that Charlie looked like he had been losing some weight. "You are getting a little skinny there, Charlie. You have been losing weight, haven't you?"

Charlie answered without turning around. "Oh, a little perhaps." "Well, don't waste away on me." He also noted that Charlie's gait had slowed a little since the first time he had met him.

When they reached the workshop, Michael waited in the main area while Charlie went back into his office area. Soon Charlie emerged with a single sheet of paper. He handed it to Michael, who looked at it.

On it was a simple list under the heading, *Books Everyone Should Read*:

1. The Bible
2. *How to Read a Book* by Mortimer Adler
3. *My Utmost for His Highest* by Oswald Chambers
4. *As a Man Thinketh* by James Allen
5. *Seeds of Greatness* by Denis Waitley
6. *Seasons of Life* by Jim Rohn
7. *The Pursuit of God* by Acden W. Tozer

"Okay, this looks interesting. Which one should I start with?"

"I'll make that one easy," Charlie said as he opened a drawer in an old metal desk that had various tools sitting on it. He reached in and pulled out an old, worn, and obviously well-read copy of *The Magic of Thinking Big*. This one is free, so you won't even be able to excuse yourself because of the cost," he said with a sly smile.

Michael reached out and took it. "Okay, then. *The Magic of Thinking Big* it is. I will definitely read it, and when I am done, you will continue to teach me the Pillars of Success?"

"That I will, Michael. That I will."

With that, Charlie grabbed Michael and gave him a big bear hug. He then pulled away just long enough to look Michael in the eyes. "That I will."

As Michael pulled out of the gates that day, he noticed a new feeling in him. He felt such warm feelings for the old man, Charlie. He was almost becoming a father to him, which was fine with him because he had lost his own father when he was ten. He never got to learn these lessons from an older man. He was cherishing the time he got to spend with Charlie, even if it was learning the wealthy Mr. Davis's Pillars of Success secondhand.

Michael looked at the book lying on the passenger seat. *Okay, I guess it's time to think big.*

# 8
## All of Life Is Sales

*"One key to having influence with others is to have others perceive you as a person of talent and virtue."*

It had taken a month, but Michael finished the book that Charlie had made "required reading." Michael had enjoyed it more than he thought he would. Now he was excited to get back to Twelve Pillars and meet with Charlie again. He was getting addicted to this personal-development stuff.

After two rings, the phone was picked up by Charlie.

"Charlie, this is Michael. How are you?"

"Terrific, Michael, how are you?"

"Fine. Better than fine, actually. And guess what book I finished reading?"

"That is fantastic, Michael. Did you enjoy it?"

"I did. And, as per our agreement, now you can continue to teach me about the Pillars of Success."

"I would love to, Michael. When can you come over next?"

"I will be in that area on Wednesday. Can I pop over for some coffee for a half-hour or so, midafternoon, say around three?"

"Three it is. I will leave the gate open for you and I will most likely be in the workshop. See you then."

"See you then, Charlie. Thanks."

When Wednesday afternoon came, Michael did find Charlie right where he said he would be—in his workshop. Michael supposed that Charlie loved it there. All alone, tinkering with things, fixing them up to usefulness again. Managing a property like Mr. Davis's would certainly be a full-time job.

There were a couple of chairs in the far back of the workshop that Michael had never seen before. They sat right in front of a window that overlooked a large pond. Michael had never noticed the pond before either. They sat down with a cup of coffee, knowing that Michael didn't have a lot of time in between sales calls.

After a brief conversation about what Michael had learned from *The Magic of Thinking Big*, Charlie moved quickly into the next two lessons from Mr. Davis's Pillars of Success.

"I know you don't have a lot of time today, Michael, but I want to share with you two more of Mr. Davis's Pillars of Success. The first is about sales and the second is about money."

"Okay, I am ready."

"Mr. Davis always says, 'All of life is sales.' That is so true, Michael. You are in sales, aren't you?"

"Yes, I am."

"Are you very good at that?"

"I used to think I was, but based on my performance, I am beginning to wonder."

"That's okay, Michael. Anyone can get better at sales if they apply themselves. The first thing to realize is that everything is sales. And to better understand it, to give a broader application of this principle, it is better to understand sales as the concept of influence."

"Influence?"

"Yes. You see, Mr. Davis says that influence is the key to a successful life. Anyone who wants to succeed must learn the art and skill of influencing others. When they do that, they will be successful."

"How's that?"

"You see, all of life is lived with other people, not in a vacuum. When you need to succeed, it is usually dependant upon working with or through other people. That is why you must influence. It is true nearly from the time we are born."

"I don't know what you mean," Michael said quizzically.

"Think about it. From the time we are born, successfully reaching our goals is dependant upon influencing others. And as we grow, we hone those skills. A baby must influence his or her parents to feed him. A child influences his or her parents for a bike. A teenager has to influence the person they fancy so they can get a date. The person who graduates college must influence their potential boss to give them a job. Salespeople must influence prospective buyers—if they want to eat well! You see, all of life is sales, and all of sales is influence."

"That makes sense…. But how do you influence?"

"There is a plaque in Mr. Davis's office that quotes Thomas Jefferson. It says, *There is a natural aristocracy among men, the grounds of which is talent and virtue.*"

"Okay… I don't get it."

"This is fascinating, Michael. If you think about the founders of America, they had come from a place where there was an aristocracy based on the monarchy. Aristocracy was passed from generation to generation. You became wealthy and had influence based solely on what family you were born into. Jefferson was speaking of the beauty of America, namely that anyone can achieve a natural aristocracy—the maximum levels of success—if you master the ground of achieving it: talent and virtue."

"So what does that have anything to do with sales and influence?"

"Michael, if you want to sell more and make more money, you have to become a better influencer. And the key to influencing others is to have others perceive you as a person of talent and virtue. Mr. Davis says frequently that talent and virtue are the same as character and skill. Be a person of strong character and increasing skill, and you will always be growing in your influence. And do you know the best way to have people perceive you as a person of talent and virtue?"

"No, what?"

"Be a person of talent and virtue." Charlie chuckled out loud at his own joke. Michael grinned at having been caught in that one. "Talent and virtue are the foundation of successful influence and sales, whether you are selling a product or selling yourself—and a successful person is always selling him or herself. Once you have mastered those, the skills of sales are pretty simple."

"Okay, I'll bite. What are the skills of sales?"

"Know your stuff. Talk to lots of people. Be persistent and never take 'no' for an answer."

"Can you explain it a bit more?"

"Sure. First of all, know your stuff. Mr. Davis says, 'You cannot speak that which you do not know. You cannot share that which you do not feel. You cannot translate that which you do not have. And you cannot give that which you do not possess. To give it and share it, and for it to be effective, you first need to have it.' If you are going to sell a product, you have to know it, believe in it, and feel it. And the same is true if you are selling yourself.

"As for talking to lots of people and succeeding in sales, simply talk to lots of people every day. And here's what's exciting—there are lots of people!"

"Just talk to lots of people?"

"Obviously they have to be qualified people. You can't just go willy-nilly. But Mr. Davis always talks about the law of large numbers, which means that a certain percentage will work with you or buy from you. If ten percent do, then you will sell more if you call forty people a day than if you call ten people a day."

"That makes sense. What was the last one again?"

"Never take 'no' for an answer."

"That's right."

"Michael, salespeople should take lessons from their kids. What does the word 'no' mean to a child? Almost nothing!"

"Hah! I know that better than anyone. When they want something,

they ask and ask and ask!"
"The idea is that most people just aren't persistent enough to succeed in sales, or life for that matter."

"Yeah, I guess you're right."

Charlie started to get up for some more coffee. As he got up, he stumbled and landed on one knee. Michael jumped up to help.

"Are you okay, Charlie?" he helped him get back up.

"Yes, I am okay. Just getting weak as I get older." Michael sat back down as Charlie poured more coffee. "Want some more?" he asked, holding the coffee pot up.

"No, I am okay."

As he walked back over to the chair, Charlie continued. "Yes, Michael, age gets even the best of us. I am not much longer for this life."

"Don't say that, Charlie, you are in good health."

"I have my days. Regardless, eventually age gets us all, if not disease before. Time is shorter than any of us would imagine. If more people would wake up to that fact, more people would live differently."

"Yeah, I imagine you are right. Life has passed me by so far. The day-to-day just lulls you to sleep if you aren't careful—and I haven't been."

"But you are changing."

"That I am. Thanks to you—and the mysterious Mr. Davis. By the way, do you think I will ever get to meet him?"

"Oh, he is around. When the timing is right."

# 9
# Income Seldom Exceeds
# Personal Development

*"What you become directly influences what you get."*

Michael's coffee was getting cool, so he decided he would have that next cup that Charlie had offered. He got up and poured himself another and as he was walking back he asked Charlie to teach him the next Pillar of Success.

"Yes, Pillar number nine. You will like this one. It has to do with money."

"If it has to do with money, you bet I'll like it. But how come it's number nine? Shouldn't it be number one? After all, money makes the world go 'round."

"Michael, this is one of the mistakes many people make. In all actuality, money doesn't make the world go 'round."

"You couldn't tell from looking at this house."

"On the surface, that is what many people think of the rich. But for the vast majority of the wealthy, money isn't the number one thing in their lives. They have had money and realize that life still goes on, just as it did before. They may live in nicer homes or drive fancier cars, but life happens to everyone. Money doesn't solve the problems of life."

"Well, I would sure like to give it a try."

Charlie laughed. "Michael, no doubt you will have the opportunity. You are learning a lot that will change your life."

"I hope so. I have always wanted to be a millionaire."

"Really? Why?"

"For starters, security."

"Money provides no security, Michael. If you are hoping for security in your wealth, you will have a long wait."

"Why's that?

"Money can always go away. You can lose it. You can get sued. Inflation can eat away at it. It can be stolen. Every year, you hear of what were once millionaires and even multimillionaires having to file for bankruptcy, going from hundreds of millions of dollars to nothing… in one year. Imagine that."

Just as he was saying the last few words, Charlie began to cough. It got so bad he excused himself to the bathroom. Michael sat there, alone, wondering why he would want money so badly. When Charlie got back, they continued.

"Sorry about that. This persistent cough; it's terrible. So, why else would you want money, Michael?"

"Well, I guess for all of the nice things it can buy me and my family."

"Yes, when I look at Twelve Pillars, I see a beautiful house. And the cars in the garage are nice. But here is what Mr. Davis says. He says, 'After you become a millionaire, you can give it all away because what's important is not the million dollars; what's important is the person you have to become in the process of becoming a millionaire.' "

"Give it all away? He didn't give it all away."

"No, you don't have to give it away. You can give it all away, because you have become a person who could get it back. Making the million dollars took personal growth to get you there. Now you could do it again if need be. That is another thing Mr. Davis teaches people. He says, 'Income seldom exceeds personal development.' If you want to make a million dollars, you had better grow personally to the point where you are a million dollar person. You have to love what you become, not love money. You know what the old proverb says—'Whoever loves money, never has money enough.' "

Michael looked up at the ceiling and leaned back in his chair. "I just wish I knew how to make more money."

"Okay. I can tell you one of the greatest secrets to wealth building the world has ever known. Virtually every wealthy person who has ever lived—save for a few, yes—has proven this principle true."

"What is it?" Now Michael leaned in

"This one is one of Mr. Davis's favorites. He says, 'Profits are better than wages.' " Charlie said it and then just let it sit there. He had a very satisfied look on his face. But Michael didn't get it.

"Profits are better than wages?"

"Yes, profits are better than wages."

"What is that supposed to mean?"

"Michael, it is simple. Do you want to make a million dollars in one year?"

"That would be great!"

"If you sold ten times what you do now, would you make a million dollars in one year?"

"Not even close."

"What about the owner of your company. If all of his salespeople sold three times what they do now, do you think he would make a million dollars in one year?"

"I think he makes a million dollars a year now, so I would imagine the answer is yes. But what does that have to do with it?"

"You are on a wage system, Michael. The owner of your company is on a profit system. And, as you yourself have just described, profits are better than wages."

"So how do I get profits rather than wages?"

"You must work for yourself. As long as you work for someone else, you won't make that much money. Sure, there are the professional athletes and the upper echelon of corporate America, but there are so few of those, that it is statistically insignificant. Ninety-nine percent of the wealthy became wealthy by working for themselves and capturing the profits. Even those who inherited their wealth, if you trace it back, it almost always ends up beginning with someone who owned the company."

"At my age, I don't know if I could go out and start over."

"Then you're stuck, I guess." Charlie was prodding Michael now.

"Well, you don't have to give up so fast," Michael countered.

"I'm not giving up. I am just agreeing with what you say. If you won't go start over, then you are stuck." Charlie paused and then began a new thought. "There is an alternative to just quitting and starting all over."

"What's that?" Michael asked.

"It is another of Mr. Davis's principles of money and wealth. Maybe the beginning of the answer to your dilemma is to, as Mr. Davis says, 'Work full time on your job and part time on your fortune.' Maybe you should start a business on the side and grow it until it is at a point where you could do it full time."

"Well, that may be a viable idea. I have had a few ideas that I have wanted to do from time to time, and yet I have never done them. What with the family and all, it would just be too hard."

"Anything of significance is going to be hard, Michael. You may as well accept that. Remember: the Pain of Discipline or the Pain of Regret. Your choice. Do you want to work hard, start your own business, grow it into a great enterprise, and then achieve financial independence, or do you want to stay where you are and hope the government has enough money to dole a little bit to you each month?"

"I would like to have financial independence—whatever that means."

"Financial independence is the ability to live from the income of your own personal resources. That is it in its basic form. You either pay yourself, or you get paid by someone else—now and in the future."

They sat there for a few moments, letting the lessons of Mr. Davis's wisdom sink in.

Charlie looked at his watch and realized he needed to get going. "I have a doctor's appointment in forty-five minutes, so I need to call an end to our meeting. But you think about these things, Michael. Remember, all of life is sales, and income rarely exceeds personal development. That should hold you over for a while."

Michael got up and put on his windbreaker. "Yeah, that should hold me over. Lots to think about this time—as always."

"You give some thought to starting one of those businesses. Then you can apply both of today's lessons—sales and money."

"All right. I will. Hey, by the way, this time let's set up our next meeting. I have to come out this way three weeks from today. Would that work?"

"I think so. I have a part on order to fix the gate mechanism. It is wearing out. That should be here around then. Maybe you could stop by when I am doing that. Should make for lots of fun."

"Well, let's plan on it, but I'll call a few days before."

"Sounds good, Michael." And then before Michael left, Charlie gave Michael a hug. They were becoming friends.

# 10
## All Communication Brings the Common Ground of Understanding

*"Communication is two or more people working together to find the common ground of understanding. And when they find that common ground, they are positioned to have tremendous power together."*

Three weeks later, when Michael pulled up to Twelve Pillars, there was Charlie, the gates swung wide open, and what looked like grease halfway up to his elbow. Michael parked just inside the gate and walked up to Charlie.

"I would shake your hand, but you wouldn't want a greasy palm."

"This time, I agree with you."

"Well, you won't be much help then, will you?" Charlie said, smiling.

"I can be your tool hander-overer," Michael said, impressed with his new word.

"Hander-overer? I haven't heard that one before."

"Oh yeah, I am one of the county's best tool hander-overers. Been practicing for years."

"I'll be the judge of that. Come on over, and I'll show you what I am doing. Each of these gates weighs over 1,000 pounds. Today they would be made much lighter with more modern materials, but that's what was available when it was done. Because of that, it has a huge motor and mechanism. I knew that I needed to replace some of the bearings and repack them. That's what the grease is for. It's kind of messy, but necessary. Boy, Mrs. Davis would have a fit if she couldn't get out to do her shopping if I let it break down!"

"I have never met her either. What is she like?"

"Oh, a fine lady. Very beautiful. Treats her husband like a king. There is a great marriage in that house. But enough about that. You are here to work and to learn the next two Pillars of Success, right? Let's see…. There are three more, so we are at numbers ten and eleven."

"That's right. At least by my calculations."

"Let's start with number ten then."

"Okay."

"First, hand me that seven-eighths wrench there behind you."

Michael dug a bit to find it and then gave it to Charlie.

"Nice hand-over."

"I told you."

Charlie went to work but talked over his shoulder. Michael wasn't much for mechanics so he enjoyed looking on and seeing what he could see.

"Number ten is all about communication. Mr. Davis always says that since success is based on human relationships, and communication is the foundation for people working together, it is extremely important. In fact, he says, and I quote, 'Communication is two or more people working together to find the common ground of understanding. And when they find that common ground, they are positioned to have tremendous power together.' If you think about it, that is so true, whether it is talking about a marriage relationship, a business relationship, or parents talking with their children."

"You see, Michael, people are so different, even the ones who like each other. And when we get to moving forward in our relationships, it can be hard communicating when times are going well, let alone when times are not going so well."

"Yeah, I know about that firsthand. It seems like Amy and I are from different planets. She talks and I can't get it, and then I talk and she can't get it. I just don't get it. And then I go to work and the same thing happens with my boss."

"I see. Well, that happens with everyone really. Communication is hard. But one of the reasons that it is hard is because so many people aren't looking at it as a practice wherein two people are trying to find common ground. Most of the time, each person is fighting to get the other person to give up their ground and come over to his or her ground. Then it is a turf battle. Instead, each should look for the common ground."

"That is a good point. I know that with Amy, I think we just try to get each other to come over to our side."

"But I bet it wasn't like that when you were dating, or first married was it?"

Michael laughed. "No, it was more like, 'No honey, how about your way. No, let's do it your way.' "

"That's human nature for you. It happens frequently. You were much more likely to try to find the common ground and work with and defer to each other because you were still trying to close the deal. Close the deal—get her to marry you. It's classic."

"Yeah, I agree."

"So, if you want to communicate well with Amy, or anyone for that matter, work to find common ground. And it will be work."

"Oh, believe me, I know that. Communication is just so difficult."

"Mr. Davis always says, 'Communication isn't just what you say. It is also how you say it, when you say it, and the receptiveness of who you say it to. And that's just the half of it. The other half is making sure you really listen.' So it isn't just the meaning of the words. It is tone—are you talking down to the person? It is timing—I'll bet Amy always wants to talk about relationships during the football game, right?"

"Yep. And to be fair, I am always interrupting her when she is trying to watch a love story."

"Michael, you are sounding downright stereotypical."
Charlie chuckled.

"It's true. I'm not making it up."

"And you have to make sure that the person is ready to hear what you have to say. If they aren't, save it. Say it later."

"Yeah, I have learned that the hard way."

"But the most important thing about communication is listening."

"Sure, we have 'listening skills' seminars at work about every other year."

"I am sure those are valuable, but it isn't the skill that is the most important. It is the character behind the skill. First and foremost, you have to care enough and value the other person enough to *want to listen*."

"Well, don't you want to listen if you are listening?"

"Michael, this is a perfect point. Mr. Davis always says that most people aren't listening, they are merely waiting for the other person to take a breath so they can interrupt them and speak their own mind."

"I guess that's true."

"What would happen, Michael, if you were actually listening rather than just waiting for Amy to take a breath so you could jump in with the alternative opinion? What would happen if you tried to see it her way and understand her? I'll tell you what would happen—it would change the nature of your marriage. And if people in general would catch this, it would revolutionize the world." Charlie paused long enough to turn to Michael, holding the wrench toward him and say, "Here's the wrench, now can you hand me that rag?"

Michael did as he was asked and then pondered what Charlie had said while Charlie was cleaning up the casing.

"I agree with you, but that is a huge job. I mean, Amy and I can do it, because we can agree to do it together, but what a job it would be to get everybody doing that. How could that be done?"

"That is a very good question, and it is a perfect segue to the next Pillar of Success."

"Oh? Do tell."

# 11
# The World Can Always Use
# One More Great Leader

*"To lead others is to help them change their thoughts,
beliefs and actions for the better."*

"Mr. Davis is very interested in leadership and that is the eleventh Pillar of Success. He always says, 'The world can always use one more great leader.' "

"That's true, I guess, but what does it have to do with me, the little guy?"

"That is the fascinating thing, Michael. Leadership is such a misunderstood concept. Most people, when they hear the term 'great leader,' think of people who lead nations, corporations or social movements. Mr. Davis says that anybody can be a great leader because all leadership means is that you have mastered the art of influencing others—sort of like the principle we talked about when we talked about all of life being sales. To lead others is to help them change their thoughts, beliefs and actions for the better."

"And that means what for me?"

"It means that if you are in a position to influence others, say Amy and the kids, or people at work, or your clients, then you should desire and work on becoming a leader in life. Not only because you will make a difference, but it is also leaders that enjoy the most out of life. Leaders make a difference, rise to the highest levels, enjoy the bulk of the wealth and have the best relationships. Leaders experience life to its fullest."

"Okay, but how do I become a great leader?"

"It starts with the principles of influence we talked about a while back, that being character and skills, so that is a start. Sales and leadership are similar, both rooted in influence. Beyond that though, there are a few principles that Mr. Davis talks about. One thing he says often is, 'Managers help people see themselves as they are. Leaders help people see themselves better than they are.' And one thing you will see is that those at the midlevel are managers, while those who rise to the top are leaders—and it reflects in their pay and responsibilities. If you want to get paid more, bring more value to others by becoming a better leader."

"Can you explain it some more?" Michael asked.

"Sure, think about it. When you talk to Amy, or one of your clients, do you talk about what is, or what could be? Leaders talk about what could be. And then they take the steps to help the people become what could be."

"I see now. But one problem I have seen with so-called 'leaders' is that they are usually brash people, who are full of themselves. I don't want to become one of those people."

"And rightly you shouldn't. But those people are the minority, even though they get the most press. There are millions of great leaders who are making a difference around the world who aren't that way. Here is the key: Mr. Davis says, 'The challenge of leadership is to be strong, but not rude; be kind but not weak; be bold but not a bully; be thoughtful but not lazy; be humble but not timid; be proud but not arrogant; have humor but without folly.' You see, the bad characteristics are just good ones taken to the extreme and used for selfish reasons."

"That makes sense."

"There is another leadership principle that Mr. Davis says is important. He says, 'Learn to help people with more than just their jobs: help them with their lives.' Great leaders are interested in people in general, not just for what they can get from them."

"So what does Mr. Davis say are the characteristics of leaders? I mean, what can I work on?"

"You can start by working on everything we have talked about so far." Charlie then ask Michael if he would hand him a screwdriver.

Michael handed over a long Phillips screwdriver while he continued. "Sure, I will do that, but what specifically in regard to leadership?"

"Well, he talks about integrity of course. The leader-follower relationship is built on trust. No one will follow you if they don't trust you. So take a close look at your life and make sure it is filled with integrity. Make sure you practice what you preach, as they say. He also talks about optimism. People want to know that where you want to take them is better than where they currently are."

"But what if where you are isn't good? How do you paint a better picture?"

"You have to know where you are going. That is another thing Mr. Davis always talks about: vision. 'Great leaders have optimistic vision,' he says. A leader knows where they are, that's realism. But they also know how to get to a better destination. That is an optimistic vision."

"Okay, help me apply that to me."

"Sure. Take your marriage for example. What would you like it to be? Create a vision for what it could be, knowing what it is, and then communicate that vision and begin to work on it. It works in any situation. Create a positive vision of the future, develop a plan to get there, communicate it, and then work on the plan."

"Sounds easy."

"Oh, it's not easy my friend. It isn't easy at all." Just as he said that, Charlie finished screwing on the faceplate that covered the mechanical housing for the gate. "Certainly not as easy as fixing a gate," he said with a proud smile. He picked up a solution for cleaning his hands, used it, and then dried them off with a towel he had brought with him.

As Charlie was putting the tools away, Michael remembered that Amy had asked him to stop at the grocery store and pick up spaghetti and sauce for dinner that night. Calculating the drive back and a stop at the store, he knew that he should get going.

"Well, Mr. Charlie, as always, you have given me much to think about."

"And much to apply," Charlie said.

"Yes, and much to apply. I should get going though. Amy and I are alone tonight. Her mom is watching the kids until tomorrow, and so we are going to cook spaghetti and watch a movie together. Should be fun."

"Yes, it should. It is good that you have some alone time with just the two of you."

"Listen, Charlie, I don't know when I will be able to get back out to hear the last Pillar of Success. I have a six-week company sales trip all through the Southwest that I have to take, interspersed with trainings, and then I will be pretty busy when I get back, just trying to catch up. But I will make sure to get out here soon after I get back."

"Be sure to do so. The last one is very important—and special."
"That's intriguing. Now I will make sure I get back out here as soon as possible."

"You do that."

"Do you want some help with the tools, getting them back to the workshop?"

"No, you go ahead, I'll be fine."

And so Charlie took the tools back to the workshop. Michael sat in his car for a moment, watching the old man slowly make his way, trudging along in that same old pair of white coveralls that he always wears. When Charlie went through the door, Michael turned the car around and went to the store.

# 12
## Leave a Legacy

*"Live a life that will help others spiritually, intellectually, physically, financially, and relationally. Live a life that serves as an example of what an exceptional life can look like."*

It had been three and a half months since Michael last saw or talked with Charlie. After his six-week sales trip, things had just gotten really busy and it seemed like he was never in the area of Twelve Pillars. One day, he just decided that he needed to hear the last Pillar of Success, so he decided to clear his schedule and take a trip out to see Charlie. He figured he would surprise Charlie and was sure that he stayed around Twelve Pillars most of the time so there wasn't much chance he would be gone.

As Michael arrived, the gate was closed.

Michael pulled up to the intercom next to the entrance and pushed the button that rings the house. A distinguished gentleman answered. "Yes, how may I help you?"

"I am here to meet with Charlie. My name is Michael Jones."

"Just one moment, please," the voice said. Michael wondered if it was Mr. Davis.

After about thirty seconds, the intercom came alive again. "Please make your way to the front of the house. Mrs. Davis will meet you at the front door."

*Now that is* **really** *strange.* The gates opened, and Michael made his way down the driveway and parked right in front of the walkway that led to the front door. After getting out, he walked slowly up the walk and up the few steps. He had never been to the front door before.

Just as he reached the door, it opened and there stood an elegant older woman, impeccably dressed, a walking advertisement for class.

"Good afternoon," she said. "You must be Michael."

"I am. Are you Mrs. Davis?"

"Yes, I am."

"It is very nice to finally meet you. I have heard so much about you and Mr. Davis from Charlie." She didn't respond and so after a brief pause Michael continued. "I am here to see Charlie. Is he here?"

"Michael, I am so sorry to have to tell you this. Charlie passed away last week. He had terminal cancer, and it finally got the best of him."

Michael was stunned. He had a hunch that something was wrong with Charlie, but he just figured it was old age that was catching up to him. "Oh my. I… I am so… I am so sorry to hear that. I had no idea. I was just with him maybe three months ago."

"Yes, the last six weeks he went really fast. Things turned and it went quickly."

The two of them just stood at the threshold of the door, not saying anything for a moment.

Finally, Mrs. Davis broke the silence. "Please come in. I have something to give to you." Michael followed her into the grand foyer and then to a room to the right. "Come into my husband's office and sit down for a moment." Mrs. Davis pushed open an ornate door that opened into the most incredible office he had ever seen. It was deep mahogany with leather chairs, bookshelves everywhere, and exquisite artwork on the walls.

But what shocked Michael the most was the large oil painting of Mr. Davis above and behind the desk. Michael and Mrs. Davis stood before the desk and looked up.

"He didn't tell you, did he?" She asked with a small smile on her face.

"No," Michael chuckled, "he didn't."

"I don't know why he always did that. He thought people would listen better to his ideas, I guess. He made a game of it." She reached out and touched Michael's arm. "With good intentions, of course."

"Yes, of course."

Together they stood looking at Mr. Davis—Charlie in a suit and tie.

"How did you ever get Charlie to sit that long in a tie?" Michael asked.

She smiled. "Believe it or not, for many years Charlie wore ties to work. But he loved it when he retired and he could putter around the home in those gardener's coveralls."

She walked around the desk and opened a drawer where she found and removed a white envelope. "He left this for you. He didn't know if he would make it to teach you the last lesson—those 'Twelve Pillars' he called them. This is the most important one. It ties all of the others together and brings purpose to them." She handed the envelope to Michael. "Sit down, and I will leave you alone to read it. Would you like something to drink?"

"No. No, thank you. I'll be fine," Michael replied as he sat down in the chair.

Mrs. Davis closed the door quietly behind her as she left and Michael was alone. Michael held the envelope and looked at the front. His name was handwritten on it. He could hear the slow ticking of the grandfather clock in the corner. Tick, tick, tick. Time passing. It made sense now to Michael. Charlie losing weight… the cough… his fatigue…. He had figured Charlie was sick, but not *terminal*.

Michael looked at the wall and noticed the plaque that Charlie had mentioned: *There is a natural aristocracy among men, the grounds of which is talent and virtue.*

Finally, after sitting in Charlie's office alone for a few minutes, he opened the envelope, took the paper out and began to read.

*Dear Michael,*

*If you are reading this, then it means that I am no longer here. I wanted to share the final Pillar of Success with you personally, over coffee in the workshop, just like old times. But the very fact that I am not here makes the case for how important the last Pillar is.*

*One thing I realized this past year is how short life is. It seemed like just yesterday that I was a schoolboy, playing with my friends. It seems such a short time ago that I fell in love with Sandra and we began our family. By the way, you finally met Sandra, I'm sure. She is a beautiful and incredible woman, Michael. I was so blessed to have shared this life with her.*

*Such a short time ago, I was building my businesses and selling them, building my fortune. And even when I finally retired fifteen years ago it felt like I had so much time left.*

*The brevity of life is its biggest surprise, Michael.*

*So what to make of all of the Pillars I have taught you so far—the very Pillars of Success that have guided my life so well? They all wrap up nicely and are perfected by the final Pillar.*

*Leave a Legacy.*

*We are but breezes of wind that blow through this world. Here one day, gone the next. No one knows how long they will live.*

*You cannot choose how long you will live, Michael, but you can choose how well you will live.*

*I believe that how well you live is bound inherently with how much you leave for others who come behind you and follow your path.*

*I never was a self-made man, Michael. I do not believe that there is such a thing. I believe that each one of us walks along the path that has been prepared by others who have gone on before us.*

*My goal in life has been to live it in such a way that it would serve those who have come after me, to blaze a trail that would allow others to move forward in their lives faster than if they had to blaze that trail themselves.*

*It has been my job to leave a legacy by teaching others the Pillars of Success—and not just to teach them, but to live them. My actions are the proof that my words are true. Michael, we must live out the philosophies we passionately believe in and have been sharing with others. In doing so, we give them the credence they need to be effective.*

*So many people waste their short lives here and then spend their final days weighted down with regret. There is no more time to go back and redo their lives. There is nothing left but a wish for more time—a wish that will never be fulfilled.*

*Michael, we all have two choices as we live: We can make a living or we can design a life. There are many who spend their lives making a living. They go off to work each day with no vision for what their lives could become. And before they know it, their lives are over. And some are so fearful that the dreams they do have will forever go unfulfilled because they never have the courage to take a risk that would enable them to reach their goals and live their dreams.*

*You can be different, though. You can design your life. Yes, it would have been better if you had started earlier—the earlier the better—but at forty years old, you have a good forty years left. You can accomplish tremendous things in your remaining years if you will design them before you live them. What will make them powerful will be if you design a life based on the Pillars of Success, with the goal of leaving a legacy for others to follow.*

*Live a life that will help others spiritually, intellectually, physically, financially, and relationally. Live a life that serves as an example of what an exceptional life can look like.*

*Let others lead small lives, Michael, but not you. Let others argue over small things, but not you. Let others cry over small hurts, but not you. Let others leave their future in someone else's hands, but not you.*

*Leaving a legacy is like planting a tree. As that seed grows into a tree, it will provide seeds, so that future generations can then plant their own.*

*You have your entire life ahead of you, Michael. Live it to the fullest potential that you have.*

*My legacy is fulfilled in part by teaching you how to live your best life. Your legacy will be to do the same for others. Give of yourself. Sacrifice for the good of others. Take the time to help others and to teach them. Be patient, loving, and loyal.*

*This is good-bye, my friend. I am glad to have met you. You are a wonderful young man with a kind and generous heart. You have touched my heart, and hopefully, I have touched yours with an indelible impression that will help you create your own lasting ripple.*

*Your friend,*

*Mr. Charlie Davis*

Michael set the letter on his lap and tilted his head back, his eyes closed and a tear streaming down his cheek. He rested there for a good five minutes, thinking of the words Charlie had taught him in their times together. His best years were ahead of him. Michael Jones's life would never be the same.

Soon Mrs. Davis came back into the office and sat down next to Michael. They chatted about Charlie for about a half an hour before Michael realized it was time for him to go. He wanted to get back to Amy and be with her.

Michael said good-bye to Mrs. Davis, knowing he would most likely never see her again. He thought it was amazing how people come and go in your life, each of them having a different impact in their own unique way.

Michael drove his car down the driveway, past the workshop and back though the entrance.

Was it a chance happening or a series of fortunate events that led to meeting Mr. Davis those many months ago? Either way, Michael knew his life would never be the same.

*I have the rest of my life ahead of me*, he thought. *I can make whatever I like of it. Thank you, Charlie, for teaching me that there is so much more that I can do for myself and for those around me.* Michael turned onto the road where he had run out of gas months ago, and began the journey that would become the rest of his life.

And the gates of Twelve Pillars swung closed behind him.

# Jim Rohn *(1930-2009)*
## WORLD-RENOWNED BUSINESS PHILOSOPHER

*Jim Rohn has been hailed over the years as one
of the most influential thinkers of our time, and
helped motivate and train an entire generation of
personal-development trainers as well as hundreds
of executives from America's top corporations.*

*For over 46 years Jim Rohn focused on the
fundamentals of human behavior that most affect
personal and business performance. Jim is the standard to which those
who seek to teach and inspire others are compared. He possessed the
unique ability to bring extraordinary insights to ordinary principles
and events, and the combination of his substance and style capture the
imagination of those who hear or read his words.*

*Jim Rohn shared his message with over 6,000 audiences and 5 million
people. He conducted his seminars and workshops throughout Europe,
Asia, Australia, and Africa, as well as in most principal cities in North
America. He was a member of the National Speakers Association and
a recipient of both its coveted CPAE Award, given to him in 1985 for
outstanding performance and professionalism in speaking, and the 2004
National Speakers Association Masters of Influence Award.*

To subscribe to Jim Rohn's free weekly online newsletter, and to see
his complete listing of products, go to www.jimrohn.com or send an
e-mail to subscribe@jimrohn.com, or call 800-929-0434.

# Chris Widener

## THE LEADER OF A NEW GENERATION OF
## PERSONAL-DEVELOPMENT AND LEADERSHIP EXPERTS

*Chris Widener is an example of how anyone can overcome any odds to achieve a successful life and help others achieve the same. Chris has overcome many obstacles... living through his father's sudden death when he was four, being sent away from his family to live with relatives at age nine and becoming involved with drugs and alcohol by the age of twelve.*

*Chris overcame those obstacles and has been speaking professionally since 1988 and has shared the stage with U.S. presidential candidates, nationally known television news anchors, best-selling authors, and professional athletes. He has spoken on motivation and leadership to some of America's finest organizations such as General Electric, Cisco Systems and the Harvard Business School.*

*He has authored over 450 articles and nine books, including the* New York Times *and* Wall Street Journal *best-seller* The Angel Inside. *He has produced over 85 CDs and DVDs on leadership, motivation, and success.*

*Chris is also a contributor to the Jim Rohn One-Year Success Plan.*

*Chris, his wife, Lisa, and their four children make their home in a suburb of Seattle, Washington.*

If you would like more information regarding Chris Widener's corporate booking rates, to subscribe to his free online newsletter or a complete listing of products, go to www.chriswidener.com or e-mail info@chriswidener.com or call 877-929-0439.

*Let Chris Widener and Jim Rohn help guide you on your journey through the Twelve Pillars to personal success...*

# The Jim Rohn
# One-Year Success Plan:
*A Plan of Consistent and Continual Growth!*

We have had 95% of our enrollees stay committed to a plan of consistent and continual growth in their personal and professional lives. The statistics and unsolicited testimonials are astonishing! Simply stated, in 46-plus years, we have never witnessed or been able to match the success and opportunity that The Jim Rohn One-Year Success Plan has generated.

## The **Bronze Package** includes:

1. A one-year game plan covering the 12 Pillars of Success (one per month —see below) and geared to help you achieve a 10%–40% increase in the following:

Month 1 — Personal Development – Become the person you truly desire to be

Month 2 — Goal-setting – Multiply your long-term success quotient/ clearly defined 10-year goals

Month 3 — Health – Spiritual/Physical/Emotional—Improve your looks, confidence, energy and quality and length of life

Month 4 — Financial Independence/Getting Out of Debt/ Saving/Giving

Month 5 — Relationships – Become a more effective and loving parent, spouse and friend

Month 6 — Time Management – Gain between 10 and 15 additional 40-hour workweeks per year

Month 7 — Networking/Referrals – Create more positive influence in the marketplace

Month 8 — Selling/Negotiating – Increase your production by 10% - 50%

Month 9 — Communication/Presentation – Increase every level of performance related to your company, staff and personal relationships

Month 10 — Leadership – Multiply your efforts and have a positive influence over a larger sphere of people

Month 11 — Accelerated Learning – Quickly improve your skills and aptitude to gain and retain knowledge

Month 12 — Legacy/Contribution – Take the time to apply your skills in making a difference in your community and world

2. 52 unique, weekly strategic game plans via e-mail with downloadable workbook pages.

3. Receive 12 conference calls (one per month) with a specific focus and hosted by a Premier Expert in each of the 12 Pillars of Success, including Jim Rohn, Brian Tracy, Zig Ziglar, Loral Langemeier, Bob Burg, Chris Widener and more...

4. Additional downloadable books, audios, conference calls and weekly workbook files.

## The **Silver Package** includes:

*All benefits listed in Bronze Package, PLUS:*

5. The Jim Rohn Weekend Event—Excelling in the New Millennium on 20 CDs—includes Jim Rohn, Zig Ziglar, Jeffrey Gitomer, Bob Burg (7 speakers total), Jim's complete 2-day program and 8 bonus sessions/3 days total.

# The **Gold Package** includes:

*All benefits listed in Silver Package, PLUS:*

6. 21 hours of DVDs from the Jim Rohn Weekend Event—Excelling in the New Millennium—includes Jim Rohn, Zig Ziglar, Jeffrey Gitomer (7 speakers total), Jim's complete 2-day program and 8 bonus sessions/3 days total.

7. Brian Tracy's Success Mastery Academy—16 modules

8. The Jim Rohn Leather Journal

9. Special Bonus—mini seminar conference call each quarter with an expert in a specialized field (finance, marketing, leadership, etc.)

For details, go to http://oneyear.jimrohn.com
or call 800-929-0434.

# To Order Additional Copies of
## Twelve Pillars, Above All Else
and/or *The Five Major Pieces to the Life Puzzle*
by Jim Rohn, see quantity discounts below:

## Quantity pricing for paperback:
*(Retail $12.95)*

| | |
|---|---|
| 1-9 | $9.00 ea |
| 10-24 | $7.00 ea |
| 25-99 | $4.50 ea |
| 100+ | $3.00 ea |

## Quantity pricing for hardback:
*(Retail $17.95)*

| | |
|---|---|
| 1-9 | $12.00 ea |
| 10-24 | $9.00 ea |
| 25-99 | $6.50 ea |
| 100+ | $4.50 ea |

## To order please:

1. Call 877-929-0439
2. E-mail: customersupport@YourSuccessStore.com
3. Visit us on the Web: www.YourSuccessStore.com
4. Via mail:

   **YourSuccessStore.com**
   200 Swisher Road
   Lake Dallas, TX 75065

*Prices subject to change.

# JIM ROHN RESOURCES

Jim Rohn's philosophies and influence continue to have worldwide impact. If you enjoyed this book, consider these popular Jim Rohn books and programs to inspire you to an exceptional life!

 **The Seasons of Life**

 **The Treasury of Quotes**

 **Leading an Inspired Life**

 **Twelve Pillars** with Chris Widener

 **The Weekend Seminar**

 **Three Keys to Greatness**

 **Living an Exceptional Life**

 **Challenge to Succeed**

To order, go to **www.JimRohn.com** or call **800-929-0434**.
While you're there, sign up for the
FREE Jim Rohn Weekly Newsletter!

# SUCCESS RESOURCES

## SUCCESS®
What *Achievers* Read™

Your monthly supply of
new ideas, inspiration, and
resources that will continue
to give you the competitive
advantage in life. Each
magazine comes with a
SUCCESS CD, featuring
interviews with Darren Hardy and today's
greatest achievers and leading success experts.

www.SUCCESS.com/subscribe

## SUCCESS®
BOOK SUMMARIES

SUCCESS Book Summaries
provide a sneak peek at the
content of each featured
book, with a special focus
on chapters that resonate
with entrepreneurs and
achievers. With a
subscription to SUCCESS Book Summaries, you'll receive
summaries of three featured books in printed, audio, and PDF
formats each month. By reading and listening to the summaries,
you'll know whether the books are titles you'd like to add to your
personal success library. Listen, read, and achieve more!

www.SUCCESSBookSummaries.com

Go to www.SUCCESS.com for more information.

# Gifts that Inspire and Tools to Build Your Business...

## Excerpts from the Treasury of Quotes

Jim's, Brian's, Zig's, Chris's or Denis's booklets can be given as a stand-alone gift or enclosed with a gift card or thank you note. They are the perfect addition that will have a positive effect on the recipient and are sure to be kept forever and not thrown away, like a note or business card might be.
Perfect for customers, family and friends!

Excellent for those of you involved with:

- Real Estate
- Mortgage
- Insurance
- Network Marketing
- Chiropractors
- Sales
- Training
- Toastmasters
- Doctors/Dentists
- Educators/Coaches

To order these products, or other products go to **www.jimrohn.com** or call **800-929-0434.**

## The Treasury of Quotes

Features 365 quotes on 60 topics gathered over 40- plus years of wit and wisdom from Jim Rohn. A must for your library!
Burgundy hardback with gold-foil lettering.
**Retail $20 each**
**Special $12 each**

## Building Your Network Marketing Business

**The hottest single CD ever created in the network marketing industry!**
Subjects include: Awakening to the Opportunity, Profits Are Better than Wages, The Magic of Part Time, The Set of the Sail, The Law of Averages, The Law of Sowing & Reaping, and more! Use for both training and recruiting!

*Prices subject to change.

# MORE INSPIRATION FROM
## WWW.YOURSUCCESSSTORE.COM

## CDs/DVDs
**Becoming an Authentic MVP**
– Denis Waitley (2 CDs)
**Secrets of Closing the Sale**
– Zig Ziglar (12 CDs)
**Lessons on Leadership**
– John C. Maxwell (26 CDs)
**The Compound Effect**
– Darren Hardy (6 CDs)
**The Art of Exceptional Living**
– Jim Rohn (6 CDs)
**Live Full, Die Empty**
– Les Brown (1 DVD)
**Memory in a Month**
– Ron White (6 CDs)

OVER **200** PRODUCTS Available!

### QUANTITY PRICING ON EXCERPT BOOKLETS

| Qty | Discount | Price |
| --- | --- | --- |
| 1-9 | | $1.50 each |
| 10-49 | 15% | $1.27 each |
| 50-99 | 20% | $1.20 each |
| 100-499 | 25% | $1.12 each |
| 500+ | 30% | $1.05 each |

All prices are in U.S. Dollars.
Call for discounts on quantities over 1,000.

## Training Packages
**Put Your Dream to the Test Kit**
– John C. Maxwell (3 DVDs/5 CDs/wkbk)
**The Happiness Advantage Kit**
– Shawn Achor (Book/CD/wkbk)
**Jim Rohn Weekend Event**
(12 DVDs/24 CDs/283-page wkbk)
**Strategies for Success**
– Zig Ziglar (6 DVDs/6 CDs/planner)

*For more information and to shop our best-selling products visit,*
**www.yoursuccessstore.com**

### Best-selling authors include:
Jim Rohn • Zig Ziglar • Darren Hardy • Shawn Achor • Rita Davenport • John C. Maxwell
Connie Podesta • Les Brown • Denis Waitley • Chris Widener • Ron White • Brian Tracy • And More!

200 Swisher Road, Lake Dallas, TX 75065
877.929.0439 • Fax 940.497-9799

*Prices subject to change.